damn Lucky

What Is Righteous and Worth Fighting for ...
and at What Price?

Valder Larka

with Owen Smith

HAY HOUSE

Australia • Canada • Hong Kong • India
South Africa • United Kingdom • United States

First published and distributed in the United Kingdom by:
Hay House UK Ltd, 292B Kensal Rd, London W10 5BE. Tel.: (44) 20 8962 1230;
Fax: (44) 20 8962 1239. www.hayhouse.co.uk

Published and distributed in the United States of America by:
Hay House, Inc., PO Box 5100, Carlsbad, CA 92018-5100. Tel.: (1) 760 431 7695 or
(800) 654 5126; Fax: (1) 760 431 6948 or (800) 650 5115. www.hayhouse.com

Published and distributed in Australia by:
Hay House Australia Ltd, 18/36 Ralph St, Alexandria NSW 2015.
Tel.: (61) 2 9669 4299; Fax: (61) 2 9669 4144. www.hayhouse.com.au

Published and distributed in the Republic of South Africa by:
Hay House SA (Pty), Ltd, PO Box 990, Witkoppen 2068. Tel./Fax: (27) 11 467 8904.
www.hayhouse.co.za

Published and distributed in India by:
Hay House Publishers India, Muskaan Complex, Plot No.3, B-2, Vasant Kunj, New
Delhi – 110 070. Tel.: (91) 11 4176 1620; Fax: (91) 11 4176 1630. www.hayhouse.co.in

Distributed in Canada by:
Raincoast, 9050 Shaughnessy St, Vancouver, BC V6P 6E5.
Tel.: (1) 604 323 7100; Fax: (1) 604 323 2600

A catalogue record for this book is available from the British Library.

ISBN 978-1-84850-479-0

Printed and bound by CPI Group (UK) Ltd, Croydon, CR0 4YY

Part 1

ONE

A man and two girls sit silently in a little wooden rowing boat on a large pine-framed lake. Three fishing rods reach out over the lake's tranquil surface while bobbing floats send tiny ripples of interference across the liquid mirror, warping the reflection of an azure-blue, Swedish summer sky.

Tiny ripples, a small boat, a man and two girls, a large lake framed by endless pine trees undulating over the hills and into the distance, under a clear sky that reaches to infinity.

The only sounds are the intermittent and melancholic 'plounk' of water against the hull, the occasional buzzing of courageous insects that have made the epic journey from shore to mid-lake, and echoes from the hidden wilderness at the heart of the pine forest.

Relative scale merges into the composite scene. A world without end in a timeless continuum set inside the appearance of tranquillity.

In my mind's eye I can see the same man, years earlier and closer then to his life as a boy. He's in a small boat on a river with a man who had been pretending to fish under an unforgiving African sun. At that time, he was on the first stage of an ill-fated mission.

This is a moment from my life in the present and a moment in my life from the past. In that moment on the lake with my daughters I knew I needed to tell the story of my life then; a story I'd kept to myself for years. Sitting with my girls in our little 'snipa', I wondered how I was going to talk about the life that I'd lived long before they were born.

I wondered what I'd tell them about my other daughter, the sister they'd never know.

Against the relative scale of our boat, the lake, the pine forest and the infinite sky, I wondered about the difference that time had made in the scheme of things. A tiny ripple of interference that wouldn't have even registered on the grand scale, but that had set the course for the rest of my life and left me with memories that had never once given me a full-day's break.

Maybe it was something about the deep peace I felt in that boat on that still lake with my two beautiful daughters, and the contrast felt in that moment with the turbulence of the time before that made me want to tell my story.

I looked at my girls; little angels intently concentrating on their rods, waiting for the slightest of movements to tear the life of an unknowing fish out of the water; watching for the dip of the float that would signal a fish grabbing the bait and the prospect of filling their plates with pride that evening.

Looking back, I can remember a broken man sitting on the rough wooden floor of a slow train from perdition on the final stage of that ill-fated mission.

Dust-caked and sweat-stained, a weathered khaki shirt and faded green army pants clung to his thin body, while his matted blonde hair framed his gaunt and haunted face. His bruised and bloodied feet rested alongside a pair of well-worn and battered leather boots, which lay discarded next to a coarse, canvas kit bag.

His sunken blue eyes stared at a .455 revolver cradled in his hands. It was loaded with a single bullet. As the empty goods' wagon rolled across the arid African savannah, the man's fractured mind ricocheted off the hero's journey that had brought him to that point.

Like a projectionist's lantern, harsh sunlight flickered through the wagon's moving slats, casting spells on a screen of magic dust. I remember the spectral figure of a bushman sitting by a campfire quivering in the glimmering motes, and a glint in the broken man's eyes as he recognized a loved but lost friend. His friend was carving four figures: his own children and the broken man's child.

Memories of righteous intention, of love and of the choices made that had brought the man to where he was, gleamed in the dust's fragile kinescope.

With a sudden jolt the wagon lurched, scattering the phantom spectacle. The bushman disappeared in a swirling eddy of shimmering light, but as he did he caught the man's gaze.

I remember the moment their eyes locked. In that moment, a seed was cast into the broken man's heart. A seed that contained the knowledge that when love and righteous intention stand behind the choices we make there is always truth and hope.

I remember the broken man realizing that in that seed love would live forever, born by its promise of healing.

Memories from my past, cast against a moment in the present.

On the snipa, from the distant shore in the background, I could hear sounds from the heart of the pine forest. A dark interior in which if ever you got lost you'd better find your way out quick or, failing that, be ready to test your survival skills. From my own interior, I heard a familiar voice.

'If you're gonna tell your story my man, tell it good!'

It was a voice that's been talking to me, more or less, for as long as I can remember. A voice that's both my own yet not mine, a voice that has guided me back onto the right path when I've lost my way, as I have on so many occasions in my scarred and chequered past. It's the voice of my inner-child and a companion that in my later life I've come to call 'Little Man'. It's a voice that seems to speak from what I call the 'Flow'.

The Great Flow is an endless and ancient stream running through each one of us. It's the colossal energy field behind all living things, offering us a totality of understanding should we choose to tune in to its timeless and infinite course. It asks us for patience and thoughtfulness, understanding and generosity: those qualities of human beings from which love is born.

With love we give time to time. It's the least the Flow asks from us. It's what we need to live up to in order to find peace because without peace nothing is sustainable. Without peace we're like snakes biting our tails. Venomous, we poison ourselves again and again, repeating the same cycle but with a different name and wearing a different mask.

The Flow asks us to be responsible and to cherish the knowledge it offers through its ancient wisdom. And, if we choose not to, it will show us our animal being, a primordial antecedent of our human selves, and all the reasons why that animal still lurks within each and every one of us.

My story actually started years before that boat on the African river, which led to that train from perdition. The thing is, and without realizing it, I'd been preparing myself for years for that quest that would lead me into a world so far from my homeland.

What we do from one moment to the next sets up our life's unfolding and it happens all at once. Each moment passes so quickly that it's impossible to weigh up the implications of the choices we make, but each choice sets in motion a chain of events that marks out our future and closes the door on alternate futures that might have been.

As a child, I remember living my life in the moment, with little thought for the future. My first seven years were a carefree adventure spent exploring the wilderness, which surrounded our home. The wilderness was a place of mysteries waiting to be uncovered, a place I wanted to know and a place I felt drawn to.

I remember my last summer in the suburb outside Stockholm where I lived with my parents and younger sister. At the time, I didn't realize it was going to my final summer in my wild roaming paradise and that by the next I'd be on the other side of the country having a very different experience of childhood. I had no idea that the carefree period of my early years would soon be over.

For that summer though, I was still enjoying life as an extended adventure. Two areas of forest, one larger than the other, surrounded our hometown and, as I got older and more confident, I gradually began to extend my scouting into this world of nature.

On one memorable day, during the last summer before we moved, I decided to head into the depths of the larger of the two forests. There were two reasons. I'd outgrown the smaller one and I'd heard rumours of a criminal gang hiding out in the larger that caught my curiosity. So, on a bright and long summer day I started out on my mission.

I took my blue fibreglass bow, as tall as I was at the time, and some fine wooden arrows my father had given me. In my belt I stuck a homemade slingshot that could fire a pebble 60 metres. I'd carved it from a tough and elastic Y-shaped branch with the knife my father had given me on my fifth birthday, and that my mother had forbidden me to sleep with.

The sling was cut out of a too-many-times-mended bicycle inner tube and I'd carved a zigzag design on the handle. My old man had tested it and then warned me to be careful where I pointed it, and I was.

I set out on my expedition with the knife in its sheath on my belt and the slingshot tucked behind it. Over my shoulder I carried a small leather pouch, containing just the right size pebbles, and my bow and arrows. Once on grassy ground I pulled off my sneakers and tucked them into the back of my belt.

Food and water wasn't an issue. I knew a place on the forest's edge where an underground stream surfaced, and berries and edible roots grew in the cool forest so I knew I could survive.

Feeling the ground with the soles of my feet was a big part of summer's freedom. I never thought about it, it just felt good to feel the earth with my feet. Crossing the juicy green expanse of grass and wild flowers before the forest, I kicked the amazing balls dandelions turn into when they're done flowering; sending hundreds of silk, parachute-like seeds drifting into the air.

Chasing after them I sent arrows flying ahead of me. Reaching my target, I found their round steel tips planted more than an inch into the trunk of a lone tree.

It was the best thing I knew. The peak of life at that time was taking off alone in the early morning on an adventure whose only limit was the long northern summer days and my mother's call for dinner at about 8:00pm. I had 12 hours, or thereabouts, to roam wild and free.

The forest spread out into the distance behind an outcrop of granite boulders and a steep hill where we skied and sledged during the dark half of the year. On that day I was heading to a second and larger collection of granite boulders, left behind by one ice age or other as it had melted and slowly pulled back toward the greater north, hidden among the trees in the middle of the forest. According to my friends, it was the place where the criminal members of a drugs' gang hung out.

I was curious to find out for myself if the rumours were true and to see what these people looked like. It was the early 1970s and heroin had a strong foothold in Sweden's cities. Of course, back then all I knew was that I was on a mission to spy on a dangerous criminal gang who also had guns. Guns! Above all, it was that that my radar-screen-of-a-kid's-ears picked up on.

Before I heard about the criminals' hideout I'd only ever ventured into the periphery of the larger forest in search of snakes. Sweden's woods and forests are home to many species and most of them are quite harmless. I used to catch them to slip into a friend's T-shirt or put in my mouth, before tapping someone on the shoulder and giving them a heart attack, as they turned to watch me open my mouth and see a snake slither out.

That had all been good stuff but I'd had enough of small snakes and wanted to find a viper, Sweden's only venomous snake. I never used to kill the snakes I found and always caught them the same way, by their tails. I'd swing them down knocking their heads on the ground and stunning them for long enough for me to satisfy my curiosity about their eyes, fangs, tongue and skin. I figured I could do the same with a viper, while making extra sure I swung it sharply enough to knock it out before it could twist itself around and bury its fangs in me.

My favourite place to catch them was in and around a small collection of granite boulders not far from home, where they'd bask in the sun. I'd heard there were some very big boulders deep in the forest and figured that the snakes there would probably be bigger, too. I also knew I'd have to go right to the centre of the forest to be able to spy on the criminals.

I'd first thought about going in search of the criminals a few days earlier, after I'd come across a small black bag hidden among the boulders near our apartment. Inside I'd found some headphones and cables, which set my lively imagination picturing rival gangs spying on each other. I thought one of the gangs might be planning to use the rocks as a hiding place and, since I was the only person who knew about the bag, it was up to me to spy on them to find out what they were up to.

Of course, the bag could well have had nothing to do with the gang but it gave me a reason for going further into the forest and in my child's mind, which saw everything as black and white, they were the evil enemy that I had a duty to go after.

I reached the top of the hill and started along the main path that led among the trees into the forest. A few hundred metres further on, I left it and made my way into a magical part of the forest where giant pines gave intermittent shade, splashing sunlight here and there like a careless painter wielding a mixed palate of golden light and hazy shadow.

I snuck my way as silently as I could through a landscape of bracken and giant trees' shadows, which reminded me of pictures I'd seen of the landscapes once roamed by dinosaurs; those images adding to the feelings of apprehension and foreboding growing inside me. I started to feel that this wasn't a game and the danger could be very real. My heart began to pump harder and I put an arrow to my bow.

After half a kilometre of intense concentration, keeping my eyes peeled for any movement in the undergrowth, I entered an area of gloomy shadow where the forest floor dipped. In the middle, a large anthill stuck out from the vegetation and, as I got closer, I could see the surface was churning with activity.

Agitated ants swarmed over the hill and, though I'd seen how aggressive these big forest ants would become when their home was disturbed, I was sure their activity wasn't normal. With the undulating movement of thousands of frantic ants, the anthill was literally boiling over.

Crouching down, with my bow and arrow pointing in the direction of the gang's hideout and with my ears cocked in that direction, I crossed toward the anthill, stopping a couple of metres away.

I was cautious because I knew how rapidly the ants could attack. I'd once thrown a stick at a hill like this and gone through the scary and painful experience of being attacked from all directions, as if one of them had blown a horn for the rest to go berserk and protect their fortress. I'd learned my lesson well and now stood stock-still, not moving so much as a toe while my dirty bare feet were bypassed by reinforcements coming in from the woods or crossed by investigating rangers.

I looked nervously at the large ants, as they took turns to tickle and sniff me. Luckily none of them decided to take a bite, which would have sent a signal to the others to attack. Instinct told me they wouldn't get vicious if I didn't move or get too curious.

Relaxing a little, I looked toward the hill again. Under a seething mass of ants, I could make out the thin shape of a viper, slowly twisting and turning its agonized body on top of the anthill. As if in a hell of torment, it writhed under a sea of pain. I imagined its agony and was certain the movement I could see wasn't just caused by the ants.

I felt a shiver of horror pass over me. The viper seemed to be trying to twine its life out of its own body, turning itself into knots and crooking into impossible angles, while thousands of ants gouged it with their jaws and clawed their needle-like legs into its bleeding flesh. I was transfixed.

The scene was at once incredible, amazing, frightening, horrible and as cruel as anything I'd ever witnessed up to that day. The ants were literally eating the snake alive; thousands of them biting into it to hold it down, while thousands more took pieces out of its flesh and into their fortress.

I'd seen snakes in similar situations before but never one so big and never one still struggling for life; struggling to escape the agony of a slow, brutal death. I didn't like what I was seeing and it wasn't long before I slowly edged away from the hill, making sure I didn't tread on any of its ferocious inhabitants.

I crossed the dip in the forest's floor and put my nose above its brim. Through the pines' trunks and the foliage I saw a man-sized movement about 60 metres away and, like a bird on the surface of the water having its feet grabbed by a crocodile, my head disappeared below the brim again.

My tense anticipation that had been distracted by nature's murderous beauty flooded back. My thoughts about how ants 'dug' on snakes turned to wondering about whether criminals 'dug' on little boys.

I remember thinking that I didn't want to end up like the viper, in the gang's hideout.

TWO

By the time I dared to bring my nose and one eye over the brim again all signs of movement had disappeared. All I could see among the giant pines were looming shadows and dinosaur plants, but rather than running I felt an overriding impulse to carry on into the depths of the forest.

I sat down with my back against the wall of the dip and checked my weapons then snuck out of the dip in a different place, and began to move toward my target. In retrospect, I can only wonder what ancient wisdom, which game of cowboys and Indians or war, had taught me not to simply follow the man I'd seen by the shortest, most direct and obvious route. At the time I didn't think about it. I just did what seemed like the right thing to do.

Above me, the sun was rising toward its midday zenith, making that memorable day a hot one in more ways than one. Trees rose over me, tall, strong and majestic, and I felt pathetically small in their presence but I also felt it was the way it was supposed to be. Their imposing size didn't scare me but made me feel somehow reassured. I felt as if they were on my side and that they were protecting me as they looked down at my tiny being from on high.

When my heart had found its usual rhythm again, I made my way forward. I knew I couldn't be far from my destination and, scanning the forest, I made out an outcrop of boulders between the massive tree trunks. Crouching even lower, I crept as close as I dared and found a good lookout spot among the bracken.

I must have sat there staring at the shadows and boulders in the distance for a good while, with an arrow ready in my bow but without seeing anything, not a movement, before the plants around me suddenly seemed to come alive. It's a normal sensation that often happens if you spend too long looking at something and it prompted me to move even closer, but rather than moving forward in a straight line I made a quarter turn and approached the boulders at a tangent.

I still couldn't see any gang members but the boulders were close enough to be counted. I'd been coming in from the northern side, and 50 metres away from the rocks I stopped. I'd noticed something shiny lying on the ground among the pine needles and sparse grass ahead of me. It was a syringe.

My old man had a private ambulance in those days. He'd shown me a syringe and told me about the dangers of infection, warning me not to touch if ever I found one. I pulled out my knife and buried the needle in the ground to protect any animal or man that might come that way; or boys with naked feet for that matter. As I did, I heard the low sound of men's voices.

My heart skipped a beat and I ducked into a clump of bracken. A group of men were coming. They stopped straight ahead of me and sat down on some of the smaller boulders. Even though I was bent low on one knee, I could see them clearly from my hiding place. I remained frozen like that for what felt an eternity.

Seeing one of the men with a rifle across his lap added to the sense of danger. This was more than serious. The rumours about the guns and 'drugged criminals' were true. The man with the rifle began heating something he was holding in his hand with a lighter.

One of the others pulled his sleeve up while a third tied a bit of rope around his friend's arm. I didn't have a clue what they were up to but I gripped the bow with one hand and tightened two fingers of my other hand on the string and arrow in readiness. It was almost as if the bow and arrow wanted to be used.

Finished with his lighter, the man handed something to the man with the rolled-up sleeve. I could see the sun glinting off the needle of the syringe in his hand. He pulled back the plunger and sucked up something then stuck the needle into his arm and pushed the plunger down. In the next moment he rocked forward with his arms by his side. Then, face-first, he dropped like a log onto the forest floor.

Meanwhile, without realizing it, and maybe in the tension of the moment, my fingers on the bowstring began to pull back the arrow toward me.

The man's two friends were laughing at the sight of their friend on his knees, face down in the dirt, with his backside up in the air.

Suddenly, I saw my arrow flying away from me from under the cover of the bracken and into the open toward the men. The string of my bow had scored the skin on the inside of my forearm, but it wasn't until much later I noticed the wound. At that moment I was watching my arrow. It hadn't been such a poor shot but a voice inside me was screaming at the arrow to fall short.

For a moment, the man with his backside in the air looked like he could end up being the target but the arrow landed upright in the ground a few metres from his face. I breathed a sigh of relief. The shot had been too weak to reach him.

The man's friends stopped laughing. I cursed myself for not having better control of my reflexes. I'd just blown my chance to find out more about these men. But at that point this was all secondary thinking. My instinct was to finish getting a second arrow to my bow, stand up and let it fly then 'lay my legs on my back' or, in other words, run away as fast as I could.

I had the arrow ready but the man with the rifle was now standing. He had a wary look on his face and quick as a flash I let my arrow fly and, without looking where it hit, or at the men's reactions, ran.

Looking back, I wonder where the idea to shoot another arrow came from. Maybe it was some kind of basic instinct: it was the man with the rifle or me.

I ran for my life. All I could think was that I should take the toughest way out of the forest to make it difficult for them come after me, even though it would mean going through thick and thorny undergrowth. I heard shouts behind me and the rifle go off. I imagined I could feel a bullet hit my back with a heavy, tickling sensation.

The man must have fired again because I saw bark fly from the trunk of a giant pine ahead. By the gods, did I ever run! I began to dodge like a rabbit chased by a fox. I didn't hear another shot but I never turned and, above all, never laid my legs off my back until I'd crossed into the small forest and was closer to home.

My mother always used to say I was the dirtiest kid in the neighbourhood and that morning I lived up to my reputation. My earlier-than-usual return and my more-than-usual scratched-up arms and legs and torn clothes surprised her.

My mother cared about my wellbeing in general but accepted there wasn't much she could do about the abuse of my own body, except say to that I'd heal, but tearing my clothes was another matter. We weren't made of money, as she used to say, so that I could just go tearing up my old clothes that she'd then have to stitch and patch. Unlike my clothes, my body could mend itself.

After a good scrub under the shower and a deep cleansing of my cuts and scratches with pharmaceutical alcohol, I told her my big story. She gave me a smile and a hug. There was no way I could tell her what I'd actually been up to, so I told her I'd slipped climbing on some rocks and slid into a clump of cranberry bushes, where I'd got scratched and torn by the thorns trying to get out.

A good lunch later, wearing some fresh clothes and with my mother's words in my ears telling me that she didn't want to see me again before dinner, and that till then I'd better find something safe and clean to do, and I was outdoors again.

Within a few minutes, I was standing in the middle of that big field of juicy green grass facing the forest again, but I wasn't about to go back in there. Not out of fear but more to do with a sense of having done what I'd set out to do. I felt I'd achieved something by going through with my mission that morning. I'd learned what I needed so didn't need to go through it again.

As I looked up at the giant pines, standing like sentinels at the forest's edge, I felt proud. I decided to take the little tarmac track between the little forest and the big forest, the same one I'd crossed earlier with my legs on my back, to pay a surprise visit to my father at our town's fire station. In those days, he'd been a firefighter as well as an ambulance driver.

Bra att du missade! 'Good thing you missed,' a voice inside me said.

I wondered where that second arrow *had* landed.

THREE

Something was set in motion by my experience in the forest, a part of me that would lie dormant for the next 12 years or so, while at the same time being complemented and prepared for its future awakening by the life I lived in the intervening years.

As I said before, that was the last idyllic summer spent in our forest-framed town. Moving to the west coast of Sweden marked the end of those early years of innocence and security that I took for granted.

Far from the metropolitan melting pot of Sweden's capital and, despite the country's prevailing liberalism, ideological investment in social justice and democracy, our new hometown was infused with the small-minded, parochial attitudes found in many places where life ticks over reassuringly, and change and difference are perceived as threats.

We were outsiders here, entering a relatively closed community without the status that affluence might have brought, which I could have hidden behind. I was small for my age and because of my tendency to run a bit wild my clothes were often patched, and I became a target for the local young thugs and bullies. The cruelty I'd witnessed in the forest ants, as they'd tortured and killed the viper, seemed to be transposed to the world of children and people. It came as a shock to realize that human life was as prone to arbitrary callousness as the one that I had, until then, exclusively associated with nature's wilderness.

Even at that young age, it dawned on me that we shared more in common with the animal world than we like to pretend.

Two years are a long time in the life of a child and hard knocks can end up deeply etched, particularly if there's regularity to being on their receiving end.

I've a vivid memory of walking through slushy snow-covered grass, between grey concrete buildings draped in the wet humidity of a northern autumn afternoon. By that time, I'd learned to sense where to expect an ambush. My shoulders would pitch up, my head would drop and, knowing what so often lurked in the shadows on my way home from school, I'd feel a mixture of adrenalin and anger.

Hearing footsteps hurrying behind me, rather than trying to run in vain, I slowed down to let them catch up and get it over with.

'Hey monkey-face, don't you know you should wait for us after school?' One of the three boys taunted me. They were all around the same age as me, but bigger.

Out of the corner of my eye, noticing one of the other boys coming toward me, I just managed to dodge a powerful push aimed at my back. My attacker went sprawling into the cold wet snow. Getting a wrestler's grip on one of the other two, I swung my weight backward and sent us both slamming into the ground.

Though I fought with the boy I'd thrown, I was soon overcome by hard kicks from my other two attackers. While I struggled to fight back, they forced my face into the freezing slush, pinning me to the ground with their knees and raining their fists down before finally leaving me, bruised and bloodied.

I remember wiping the blood from my nose and lips with a handful of snow, and the feelings of shame and humiliation I was always left with after being attacked. I can also remember the feelings of rage that sprang from a sense of injustice at being victimized.

As they walked off, my attackers looked back at me. I'd fought back this time. It couldn't have been as much fun for them to be on the receiving end of a punch to the nose and teeth, a knee in the balls and another to the ribs. I vowed to myself that they would never make me bend and they would never break me. From now on, each time they jumped me I'd fight back, like I just had.

Though the tears continued to run down my cheeks, I began to feel better inside. It was a feeling I never forgot.

Soon after it started, I decided to keep the fact that I was being bullied to myself. I didn't want to give more worry to my already stressed-enough parents. I knew nothing about the background to our economic situation back then, but can now see it in the context of the global recession that accompanied the oil crisis in the early 1970s.

Times were hard, and became harder the further down the heap you happened to be. We were far from destitute and my parents always made sure my younger sister and I were cared for and had food in our bellies, but my father had to work hard to make ends meet. Back then there were many nights when I held my confused and crying sister while we listened to our parents' raised voices firing back and forth over their money worries in the next room.

Our parents were good people but economics had them strapped down and they didn't want to give up on their principles. They had quite traditional values, including their belief that it was my old man's job to go out and work while my mother stayed at home and made sure my sister and I got the love, attention and care they thought she would be unable to give if she was working.

I didn't want either of them to know what I was going through at school, so I started doing odd jobs and eventually got a paper round. Earning the pocket money my folks couldn't give me to buy things helped me keep up with my peers and, somehow, not feel such an outsider.

Desperately wanting to be accepted and belong, I threw myself into sports and joined all the teams I could. I also learned how to fight by taking up competitive wrestling and martial arts.

In our home near the forest I remember the summers most of all and in our home on the west coast, the winters. Ice hockey became my passion. Its hard physicality and in-your-face toughness didn't faze me in the slightest. On the contrary, I had become used to taking a beating in my early years in our new home.

On the ice-rink during a game of hockey you weren't a victim; with equal numbers on both sides the odds weren't stacked against you. I'd begun to see that in life, the odds were stacked against some people more than others. I think I inherited this perspective from my mother.

I remember countless nights falling asleep hearing her listening to the radio while she went about her chores in the kitchen. The following morning she'd be on the war path over some injustice or other she'd heard about the night before, something in the world that was wrong or downright evil that she knew she could do little about except get hot-blooded over.

I guess it rubbed off on me and, as I got older, if I witnessed something I thought was unjust I'd make it my business to get involved, especially when I saw kids getting pushed around and bullied. I knew what it was like to be the underdog and I couldn't stand by and watch someone else being forced into that position.

When I was 12, my father signed up to work overseas with the UN in Thailand. Until then, he'd had to hold down two, sometimes three, jobs to make ends meet. For the first time since we'd moved to the west coast his leaving us for South-East Asia meant a degree of financial security.

We knew where he was going was dangerous. The war in Vietnam was only just over and civil war was kicking off in Cambodia, but we also knew he could look after himself.

Born in a harbour town in Sweden's north, he'd gone to sea when he was 12 before doing his National Service. When that came to an end he'd opted to stay on in the army and saw active service in the Middle East and Congo in the late 1950s and early 1960s, so we knew he was no stranger to danger. It was probably in his blood.

My old man's family can trace their roots way back to the days when Scandinavian people used to go 'a Viking'. The term 'Viking' is an Old Norse word that originally referred to going on an overseas expedition. It's a complete misconception to think of the Vikings as a people. They were just the men recruited from different areas of Scandinavia to take part in these expeditions.

It's more than likely that my father's ancestors were involved in expeditions into 'Rossland' – Russia – and beyond. Legend has it they even went as far as the lands populated by Genghis Khan's people and intermarried with the Mongols.

My mother's roots also go back to the Vikings. Her family came from Jutaland, in south central Sweden, another area where 'Viking' warriors were recruited. It's also a bit of a misconception to think of those Scandinavians as barbarians. Certainly the people that went 'a Viking' were warriors but they also had a pretty advanced and sophisticated culture for their day, with a strict code of honour and system of values. Something I think my parents inherited and passed on to me.

Maybe it was already in my genes, and then drawn out during the formative years of my early childhood. The code of the warrior became second nature. I'd never go looking for a fight but I'd fight to uphold a principle and to defend those I cared about.

It was this code of honour, and a commitment to the values that I felt were important, that later led me to make a series of choices that closed the door on the 'normal' life I might have had.

FOUR

By 1982 my father had been working with the UN for five years. He'd gone from Thailand to Cambodia and from there to Kenya. We hadn't been together as a family since he'd signed up but his posting to Kenya was to be different, as we were going there, too.

It was an exciting prospect. Sure, I was going to miss ice hockey and my friends but I was full of anticipation: not only about living in a different country, but also about being on a different continent.

From the land of the midnight sun to the land of eternal summer, arriving at Jomo Kenyatta International Airport in May 1982 was like a dream. I could see a land without end, stretching itself over the horizon, as the early morning heat danced across its surface.

I could see yellow grass and leaf-dressed trees under a bright, clear, blue sky and not a pine in sight.

I was just 17 and, though I had no inkling of it at the time, was beginning a chapter in my life that would take me much further from my Scandinavian homeland than the flight that had just brought my mother, sister and me from Stockholm to Nairobi.

We'd spent the previous Christmas with my father in Nairobi, so it wasn't all totally unfamiliar. I'd got used to the heat and bright blue sunlight and, maybe strangely, felt at home. Though I'd felt like a tourist during our stay at Christmas, I'd made a point of trying to get to know the people I came into contact with.

A guy who worked in the hotel where we'd stayed had taken me on a dawn fishing trip and another guy had invited me to his house for dinner with his family. I found the people friendly and easygoing. They smiled when I smiled at them, answered politely if I had a question and they liked to laugh.

Returning again, I no longer felt as if I was a tourist. We were *living* in Kenya now. I was intent on really getting to know it, rather than getting caught up in the bubble-like world that most ex-pats tended to inhabit.

We arrived in Kenya with a 12-week wait before our house in the leafy suburbs of Nairobi's Kileleshwa district would be ready to move into. So our first home was the Hotel Africana. It was a fine, three-star establishment, just up from Uhuru Park and across from the Uhuru Highway, which cut through the city; keeping the park, hotels, fine homes, state buildings, presidential palace and even a golf course on one side and downtown on the other.

After only a short while I knew the face of every member of the hotel's staff and they knew me. I even dared trying out my shaky English on them. Encouraged by the fact that no one laughed at my attempts, I started to strike up acquaintances. They were all kind and easy to get along with.

While we were in Kenya previously, I'd discovered that the average person's house was quite basic, with few of the luxuries and mod cons people in the West take for granted. Knowing that the homes of the people I was meeting shared little in common with the hotel where they worked made me feel a bit uncomfortable and gave me a niggling sense of shame.

I'd begun to get pocket money on a regular basis for the first time in my life and so I started tipping. It became a habit appreciated by those on the receiving end. The rest of the family started to follow suit. I don't know if I'm imagining it but, looking back, I think the hotel's staff felt a certain affinity with my family. Maybe they could tell that in our own way we, too, knew about the day-to-day struggle.

Our shaky financial situation in the past probably had a lot to do with my soon acknowledging the big difference between the lives of the majority in Nairobi and the bubble-like world occupied by the ex-pats.

By the time we'd settled into the hotel it was the beginning of the summer in Sweden and that meant long holidays. I had a universe to discover and weeks before I'd even have to think about school, so I began exploring Nairobi.

The people I was meeting on a day-to-day basis intrigued me and I was ready for adventure. It didn't take long for me to run into a situation that in a strange kind of way marked out the difference between my Swedish adventures and those in store for me in Africa.

One day, as I made my way downtown from our hotel, I noticed a church in the shade of some beautifully majestic jacaranda trees. I'd passed the church several times before but had never paid it much attention. I've no memory of what caught my eye on that particular day but I stopped to peek inside.

I was surprised to find the church half-full with a congregation of predominantly Indian-looking men and women talking in hushed whispers, who seemed to be waiting for someone or something. I quietly made my way inside, sat down in a pew at the back and waited with them, aware of a distinct feeling of anticipation hanging in the air.

It was almost as if they'd been waiting for me to join them for within moments the door of the church opened again and the congregation turned and fell silent. I realized how conspicuous I must have looked sitting alone in the back, but nobody was interested in me. All attention was on the four men coming through the open door carrying a woman on a stretcher.

As they processed past me up the aisle the woman on the stretcher caught me with a gaze that seemed to reach right through me. Her wild eyes looked straight into mine and she said something in a dialect so strange-sounding that the hairs on the back of my neck stood on end. I felt an icy bolt shoot straight up my spine, despite the warmth in the church.

As she was carried past the congregation, people began crossing themselves and praying and it dawned on me that the woman was there to be healed of some malady. Everything about her totally unnerved me. She seemed consumed by an internal battle, as her mad-stricken eyes went from dead to wide to rolling and back again to dead in quick succession.

I didn't know about this kind of thing at the time but later realized she was possessed and had been brought to the church to be exorcized. Nobody seemed bothered by my presence so I sat there for the next two hours, as a priest performed his rituals and the congregation offered the afflicted woman their loud prayers and heartfelt support.

Finally she was carried out as she'd been carried in. Now asleep, she seemed calm and at peace. I wonder what she'd seen when she looked through me, and what her cryptic utterance meant. Maybe it was no more than the rambling of a deeply troubled, disturbed and unhinged soul.

Looking back, I wonder if she'd caught a glimpse of the path that lay before me: a journey of which I had absolutely no inkling. Perhaps a demonic shard had leapt across the space between us when she'd caught me with her eyes. At the time though, this kind of thinking was far from my mind as I stepped onto the bustling street outside the church.

Leaving the tranquil shade and heavy scent of the purple-blossomed jacaranda trees, I walked along the busy road toward the city centre.

Despite the weird experience I'd just had, I didn't feel like a stranger nor did I intend to let myself be perceived as one. As I walked, I swore to myself that I was going to do all I could to get to know this place and its people, and to become one with the vibrant and enthralling world in which I'd arrived.

FIVE

Once I started school in Nairobi, I quickly made friends with both fellow Europeans and affluent Kenyans, but I still felt that I needed a different kind of connection in my new home. I also needed to be able to make a bit of money. Back in Sweden I'd found it quite easy to pick up work. In Nairobi it wasn't so simple.

I started supplementing my pocket money by washing our car a couple of times a week. I also did some tennis coaching with kids in a sports club near my school and helped others with their schoolwork, but it was irregular and didn't pay very much.

Then two far more lucrative ways of earning money presented themselves to me; one involved instigating drinking competitions and the other acting as a bodyguard for a Kenyan politician.

Out on the town one Friday evening with a couple of mates from school, I discovered a way to profit from the first. We'd challenged each other to a drinking competition, each of us staking 100 shillings on the basis of winner-takes-all.

As the evening progressed I began to feel increasingly woozy. I'd eaten from a roadside vendor earlier that day and, though it had never happened before, thought I might have picked up a bit of food poisoning. Not wanting to risk losing my stake, I disappeared to the bathroom.

I'd suffered from travel sickness as a young boy and my parents had taught me how to make myself vomit to relieve the nausea. Emptying my stomach of whatever nasty bacteria had taken up residence had the unanticipated side-effect of putting my beer-gauge back to zero. It was as if I was starting again from scratch. When I returned to our table I didn't mention what had happened but casually proceeded to drink my competitors under the table and win our bet.

Having discovered the technique quite by accident, I set out to make more money from it. I progressed from challenging friends in pubs to customers in Nairobi's more upmarket bars. I had two different challenges. One was simply based on the amount of beer that could be drunk before total collapse and the other, which tended to be the one I used on the guys with fat wallets, involved betting on who could down a bottle of beer the fastest.

The speed with which I could empty a bottle seemed to impress to such a degree that my opponents usually wanted to keep betting and ended up losing all their money rather than calling it a night.

Drinking at such a speed hits you fast, so I had to make sure I was aware of the first symptoms of inebriation, as they came sneaking over me – an expanding warmth in the centre of my brain that slowly impaired balance and put my capacity to think clearly in a complete spin. If I didn't stay on top of it and excuse myself to the bathroom, I could well end up the loser.

What I found astonishing was that the more people drank, the more they seemed to think they could drink, which made it easier for me to disappear to the bathroom to execute my secret technique.

I convinced myself that my marks were fair game, since I'd never told anyone they couldn't do the same, but then I never told anyone I did it either. I made sure I was careful I didn't get caught stuffing my fingers down my throat. To do so would have risked me getting into a fight, or worse getting beaten silly. Invariably, the guys with fat wallets were never alone and they were grown men, not a teenage boy like me.

I'd been at this particular game for a little while when I realized I wasn't the only person in Nairobi using the technique. There was a bar in the centre of town called simply The Pub. It was the only down-to-earth establishment in the centre of the city and became my favourite watering hole.

On my first visit, I met a group of girls who I later discovered were there on business and prowling for punters. When you're poor and job opportunities aren't that many, you've got to do whatever you can in order to survive.

Maybe they saw me as an easy target and wanted to get me drunk enough to take me somewhere I'd pass out so they could empty my pockets. As it was, I had a bet going with them and we were in the middle of the competition. When it felt like the right time I slipped off to the bathroom.

Through the thin partition walls that separated the 'Ladies' from the 'Gents', I could hear the sound of someone else throwing up next door. I'd noticed one of the girls slip off at the same time as me and realized she was using my trick. Half-drunk, I started laughing as I vomited and she soon picked up on what was going on.

Though it was an unusual way for a romance to start, it certainly broke the ice between us.

Rose was at university and had to find ways to support her studies and give herself a chance for a better future. A very pretty girl with a warm heart, she shared a 15 metres squared room, on the edge of Nairobi's slum district, with seven other girls. There were a good few times when we sneaked into that room full of sleeping bodies, after a night of successful drinks' challenges, to make love quietly; trying not to wake anybody up.

Though she didn't have any illusions, Rose still had dreams and ambitions. One night, as she was falling asleep, she told me how she'd like to meet a boy who'd ask for her hand in marriage and make her happy at home in Africa. Unlike many of her friends, she didn't want to be taken away by a white man to his 'promised land'. Then she said she hoped no war would kill me.

It seemed really strange at the time and later made me wonder what she'd seen and where that had come from.

Rose showed me what it meant to live the tough reality the majority of people in Nairobi experienced on a day-to-day basis, and also the kinds of choices the ambitious were making as they sought to realize their dreams. She seemed totally secure in the knowledge that strength of character and a sense of purpose far outweighed petty judgements and intolerance, and that being poor need never negate personal pride and self-worth.

I deeply admired her strength, will and ambition. Rose did what she had to do in order to get where she wanted to go, but without compromising her personal sense of dignity and integrity. She taught me that, despite what you may have to do to negotiate poverty, you always carry the priceless value of being alive and always have the potential to love.

My role as a bodyguard started one night during the rainy season, at the end of an evening spent at the district police station near our house in Kileleshwa. Most of the single policemen and women working there lived at the station. They spent a lot of their free time in a large communal room adjoining the station, or sitting on benches outside the 'duka' next door. A local convenience store, the duka sold basic supplies and beer.

On that particular evening, as I was walking up the dirt road that led to our house, my muddy tracks crossed those of John, a Kenyan guy who lived with us, and worked as our gardener and general maintenance man. 'Young bwana, come for a beer with me?' John asked as we exchanged greetings.

It was the end of the working week, and he'd showered and put on his best clothes, which were worn and a bit on the small side, to go for a few relaxing beers; to take his mind off a world of worries, involving the health and futures of his seven growing children.

I was on my way back from town with a pocket full of shilling notes I'd just won in one of the city's 'nicer' bars. I got on well with this lean, short man and gladly accepted his offer. His kind, but careworn face lightened and he reached his hand out for mine. We walked hand-in-hand to the police station, which was as normal a way for two men to walk in East Africa as it was to have muddy shoes with your finest clothes during rainy season.

When we reached the police station we sat outside, with off-duty police officers and other 'civilians', on the worn, wooden benches between the station and the duka. I felt totally at home in the environment and settled back to soak up the ambience and, with my limited Swahili, try to catch what I could of the local gossip.

I'd met the station sergeant before. He and two of his officers had pulled up in a car alongside me late one night while I'd been walking home from downtown. It wasn't particularly safe to be out and about after the colossuses of rough, beaten-up Leyland buses had stopped running, but since Nairobi's matatus (minibus taxis) didn't run in a straight line in the direction I was heading I didn't have much choice.

The road I had to take cut through a large area of forest that bordered the city centre and ran all the way to my part of town. It was a good three kilometres' walk and at one point forked off toward the presidential palace, which was where the sergeant and his men had been patrolling before they'd stopped by me.

I'd heard about groups of robbers that would cut down small trees and drag them across the road to use as a roadblock to ambush and rob some poor bugger silly. But I liked relying on my own two feet and always carried a large club, studded with eight-inch nails, as much for protection from the large dogs that prowled the night streets as from thugs and robbers.

The sergeant and his men had been taken aback by my club and given me a ride home. That evening, when he saw me with John on the bench outside the station house, the sergeant made a point of coming over to greet me. He joked about my club as he shook my hand and asked us to join him on his bench. By the end of the evening my club would unofficially be in the service of the Kenyan Police Force.

As John and I were getting ready to make our way home, the sergeant asked me if I'd do him a favour. He explained how one of the guys who'd been drinking with us paid him for a ride back home. The sergeant explained that the guy was a politician and a bit of a drunk. Someone in the station had been jealous that the sergeant was making money on the side and had snitched on him, getting him into trouble with his senior commander.

From that night on I'd walk the state official the kilometre back home once or twice a week. I'd sneak out of bed at three in the morning, careful to not to wake my mother, grab my club and find the man half-drunk, or worse, at the police station. Then walk, or drag, him home. He paid me well for my bodyguarding services.

The money I earned came in useful because by then I was already involved in a parallel world, on the other side of Nairobi. It was a world I'd entered wittingly but one that was going to change me forever.

SIX

Like all cities, Nairobi was a place of worlds within worlds. It was also a place where two quite distinct universes existed side by side.

I'm not quite sure how I got drawn into Nairobi's 'other' universe but maybe I was responding to the same impulse that had drawn me to the forests near my first home in Sweden. Maybe it was because, since I'd been a boy, I'd wanted to see for myself all shades of life and all corners of humanity; particularly those that tended to be pushed to one side, out of the purview of 'regular' society.

I don't think I was being voyeuristic. I didn't just want to gawp at people because they'd been labelled as 'different'. It had more to do with feeling that I shared something in common with people who'd been forced to one side. I'd known what it was to be pushed away and marked as an outsider when we'd moved from our town by the forests.

It had given me a perspective on life that made me realize that outsiders often have a clearer and broader perspective than those who only know the inside.

It was through Rose that I first became aware of Nairobi's other universe; a section of the city populated by the poor and destitute, and constructed with whatever materials were available at the right price, free, or for the taking: from broken breeze blocks and wood, to plastic and cardboard, and everything in between.

When my school friends found out that I was spending time in the city's slum district they thought it was very odd. I'd accompany them to Burgerland in the heart of downtown, where they'd go to play pinball and video games, then head off for the city's netherworld. 'It's bloody dangerous down there, man,' I remember a Kenyan friend warning me; obviously perturbed that I wanted to go anywhere near the place.

I told my friends that I'd met a girl who lived there, and not just any girl but a real African princess. They'd been suitably impressed and intrigued. It wasn't a total lie because the room Rose shared was in a tenement bordering the slum.

My friend was right; the place was 'down there', in a pit of heat during much of the year and a pool of mud during the rainy season. It wasn't far from Burgerland: along a road that led behind the restaurant, past a busy and rather dusty square that doubled-up as the long-distance bus station and down a long hill. At the bottom, where the tarmac ended, the slum began.

A hard compacted mud road continued onward, demarcating the border between the city's two universes. The mud road's surface was literally oiled and greased by all the street mechanics and spare-parts businesses that lined the entrance to the slum.

The smell of old engine oil mixed with exhaust fumes from clapped-out motors, coupled with the infernal din of men and machines, marked the city's limit. It was as if an invisible sign had been sledgehammered into the dried mud of the crossing announcing the end of one universe and the beginning of quite another: 'Abandon hope, all ye who enter here'. It might as well have been the entrance to Dante's Inferno.

Men, stripped-down and with skin smeared with the same grease and oil that slicked the ground laboured over wrecks of cars while charcoal-coated men, with muscles and sinews straining, pushed hand-trailers laden with overfilled bags of the district's primary fuel.

Half-naked toddlers and children ran around or sat in the filthy, oil-stained dirt with a look about them that suggested they weren't going to be allowed to see their fifth year. Those who survived beyond that decisive milestone seemed desperate to fulfil some sort of penny-making function. The sweating traffic of man-powered, two-wheeled trailers, struggling to bear the weight of jerry cans filled with hundreds of litres of water, weaved and swerved alongside diesel-spewing lorries crawling in and out of the large potholes that peppered the mud road.

It was life at the hard-end, where survival was a lottery ticket written in the sand. In this zone all had been lost and all may be found; anyone could be hiding inside its corrugated labyrinths of rusty sheet metal, chipped and flaking asbestos boards and rotting plywood.

The first time I found myself there I wondered why any of the slum's inhabitants would have stayed long enough to create a life amidst the squalor and bedlam. From all the human activity going on around me, it was obvious lives were being lived.

I later learned that for many it had become the place at the end of a road that had started with them selling the little land they owned in the country in an attempt to realize a dream in the city, only to end up having to sell their return ticket with those dreams.

For others, who weren't up from the country but just down on their luck, the city's slippery slopes more often than not led down that tarmac road.

Then there were the refugees, hidden and anonymous, using the slums as cover.

It was into this world, within that other universe, that the tarmac road led me.

SEVEN

I'd reached the bottom of the hill and the end of the tarmac, and was standing in the shade of a staircase between two shops that led to a last outpost of apartments at the end of Nairobi's more fortunate universe.

The staircase faced the junction where, each time I'd come here, I'd stopped to discreetly watch the buzzing life of this borderland. In that place, which my friends feared, I felt alive. I was aware that I had to move on and avoid looking like a tourist, as it would attract any hawk-eyed predators in the vicinity.

During my previous trips I'd always turned right where the tarmac ended. This time I decided to go left. My route took me along a street of storefronts. For some reason, I felt like I was walking on the sidewalk in an old town in the Wild West. Every store had a downward sloping, concrete slab below its open front. Rather than go in, customers looked at what was on sale from the counter, and bought from there.

All along the street, two rows of similar, small, filled-to-the-brim, kiosk-like stores faced each other. Some sold textiles, some TVs, some hi-fi equipment, some car spares and tools, and others just seemed to be full of junk.

Outside one, a woman was sitting on one of the concrete slabs with a small selection of candy and newspapers spread out on a piece of cardboard in front of her. I stopped to buy a packet of 'Big G' chewing gum and slowly continued on my way. I felt the eyes of an Indian-looking man following me suspiciously from behind the counter of the store.

He might have been managing the woman's meagre business; I had no idea. I did know that many black Kenyans hated the Kenyan Indians for their apparent grip on the country's business, and many Kenyan Indians seemed to despise black Kenyans. Adding to the sense of division between the two communities was the fact that the Indians preferred not to mix with the African Kenyans, and tended to segregate themselves in predominantly affluent areas.

Despite the everyday occurrences of Indian Kenyans treating African Kenyans as less worthy, there would be other examples where they worked alongside each other and showed a better side; maybe like the man in the shop.

I wondered if he'd given her a place outside his shop and a few items to sell; a little help to make a living as best she could. I wanted to think so but I was also aware that sometimes there was a thin line between helping the miserable and using their misery for personal profit.

Feeling her watching me, I turned and smiled at the woman. She broke into a smile then immediately brought her hand up to her mouth, probably to cover rotten teeth, despite her relatively young age. She turned her pretty, shy eyes back to her business. I was sure she'd been surprised but also seemed happy that I'd shown an interest in her. Something inside me cried for her, and all her brothers and sisters in a similar situation.

I nodded a greeting at the Indian man who, though similarly surprised, levelled his hand in greeting and returned my smile. Then he, too, turned away. His look was of a different kind to the woman's, I thought. Perhaps, the kind that assumed we were not 'equals', but didn't want to show it.

It was like that there. Since colonization, the whites had asserted their position on top of the human ladder for God knows how many reasons that to me were all but human. If I had a ladder it was a simple one; as simple as the fact that the woman, the man and me now knew each other. I was no longer a stranger to them and our eyes could meet in a different way the next time I passed. To me that was righteous and all well and fine; just as it should be.

A small kid ran up to me, having spotted me buying the pack of Big Gs. He greeted me with a grubby, outstretched hand. Silently asking me for a piece of gum, or anything for that matter because a *muzungu* (white man) always possessed something worth having, and his bleeding heart would often offer it up. I gave the boy a couple of pieces of the gum.

Wanting to get off the street before he had a chance to tell his mates, I ducked into a discreet entrance just off the sidewalk. Now almost completely faded, the word 'BAR' was painted vertically down a wall that led to a short flight of steps. Descending them, I found myself facing an opaque, chicken-wire reinforced glass panel set in a worn wooden frame.

I paused, suddenly wondering what the hell I was doing there and what exactly I was looking for in the slum. I let a few seconds pass before reaching for the door's handle.

As I opened the door, a room that seemed devoid of any soul or identity confronted me. Two fluorescent tubes burning in the ceiling starkly lit the bare dirty-white concrete walls, light-grey concrete floor, plain tables and chairs and worn, wooden bar. I was soon to learn that the bar's identity wasn't in its walls and furniture but in its clientele.

The people that turned to see who was entering their world looked perfectly at home in the harshly lit room. Three women were sitting at a table near the bar, while four men sat under the ubiquitous photograph of Kenya's president on the far side of the room.

The bartender, a tall gaunt man who looked like he pulled extra time on the side as a gravedigger, was leaning on the scuffed and flimsy-looking bar.

I felt eight pairs of eyes surveying me curiously, as if I was an endangered species that had lost my way and stumbled into their neck of the woods.

I nodded a mute greeting at the room in general and moved toward the bar. On cue, the three women raised their eyebrows and leaned back in their chairs. As I passed their table one of the women greeted me in Swahili.

'Hujambo, muzungu?' she said while shooting a hand straight up between my legs and grabbing my nuts in a powerful grip.

Without thinking, as a spontaneous reflex, my left hand grabbed her hand while my right darted to her nose, pinching it between my thumb and forefinger. Nobody in the room uttered a sound. It was as if we were suspended in the moment immediately before a duel.

My grandfather had taught me the nose grip. He'd used it on me on many occasions, until I'd learned to be faster than his sweet but powerful pinch and mastered the grip. I'd used it in the past to turn tense situations into humorous ones. It didn't always work but when it didn't, a fight would have probably gone down anyway, and then the surprise of the pinch usually gave me an advantage.

As on other occasions, my stunned opponent was looking down with crossed eyes at my finger and thumb. Her two friends looked from the pinch she had on my nuts to the pinch I had on her nose. From the other side of the room, the four men watched curiously.

'Sijambo mama!' I returned her greeting, the sound of my voice cutting through the tense atmosphere.

The smile that spread across her face looked rather funny with my hand planted in the middle of it, but the standoff had been broken and we both let go.

'Hello ladies! Three beers? Tuskers, right?' I asked them.

I was glad the scene had ended with smiles. The woman's 'pinch' had been done part in jest and part as way of a professional introduction. I was glad she'd taken my pinch in equal jest. I was sure the three young and sturdy mamas wouldn't have needed any help to cause some unforgettable damage and I had no idea what the four men on the other side of the room would have done if it had turned nasty.

As I continued to the bar, the ladies were still laughing at what had probably been a unique moment. Out of the corner of my eye I noticed the scene had put smiles on the men's faces, and stirred them into a low-toned conversation.

Having paid the gravedigger for four warm beers and carried them over to the women, I turned to face the men. They were all looking at me; three with lifted bottles and smiles, possibly hoping for a free round from this species with a generous pocket, while the balding and stony-faced fourth man kept his bottle on the table; fixing me with an intelligent mind, behind eyes that shone with a tiny smile they were clearly not in the habit of making.

From that moment, the bar became my second home and the people my friends; particularly Elisabeth, the woman who'd grabbed my nuts, and Moses, the stony-faced balding man.

Elisabeth was Kenyan and in her late twenties. She'd come to Nairobi with her mother and younger brothers and sisters with dreams of a better life in the city. Her alcoholic father had abandoned the family and left them destitute in their home in rural Kenya, so they'd left for Nairobi and ended up in the slum. As the eldest, it was Elisabeth's role to be the family's provider and she did what she could to support them.

She became like an elder sister to me and, though our relationship remained platonic, we developed a real bond and a mutual sense of caring and love that I'll never forget. Her life was hard and the sense of responsibility she felt for her mother and younger brothers and sisters was so great that it weighed her down; etching itself in the strain I could see on her face. But her beautiful eyes still shone brightly and she had such a good heart.

Like Rose, she was doing what she could, while always focusing on achieving a better life, but unlike Rose Elisabeth bore the responsibility for a family. The complexities involved in having to eke out a living as a prostitute and support a large family were balanced by her simple dream of being able lead a quiet life with a husband by the sea one day.

Moses was Ugandan and in his late forties. His friends were younger but also from Uganda. All were exiles; refugees from a homeland in turmoil. I soon learned about the conflict and upheaval that had displaced these men and their families to Nairobi, their involvement in the campaign to end the years of terror that gripped their country and return it to a state of peace.

An educated man, Moses had been involved in political activism and peaceful opposition: first to Idi Amin then, after he was deposed, to the repressive regime of Amin's successor, Milton Obote. As Obote began to feel increasingly threatened by popular opposition to his government, Moses had been arrested and tortured. Released to find his wife brutally raped and beaten, and his young son beaten nearly to death by government soldiers, he fled to neighbouring Kenya with his family.

Just as I'd witnessed in the forest all those years before, parallel worlds were spinning in their own orbits; so close, yet so far from the orbit of my own world. And if, for whatever reason, I felt drawn to know these worlds, with the world

I'd discovered in Nairobi's slum I wanted more than simple knowledge – I wanted to play a part in it.

The more Moses and his friends told me about the state-sanctioned terror being inflicted on vast numbers of their country's people, the more my sense of moral outrage grew. The current situation in Uganda had arisen directly from years of colonial rule in which different groups of people had been awarded different levels of rank and status according to the roles they were given in the colonial machinery.

Until the early 20th century, Uganda didn't exist. Like much of modern-day Africa it was created as a by-product of colonialism to reflect the ways the European colonizers ran their own countries. Uganda came about when Britain, the dominant colonial power in the region, incorporated a diverse range of ethnic groups into an imperialist protectorate.

For these groups, the idea of a unified bordered state was a totally alien concept. The British colonial administration instituted a policy of divide and rule; setting one group against another, as each was given more or less power and authority, and access to wealth and education, within the country's civil service, police force and military. It was no different to the way other European powers managed their colonies, but laid the stage for the conflict that was now tearing Uganda apart.

Historically, tribal monarchies and chiefdoms had dominated the region's political organization. These had been incorporated into the Ugandan government following independence in 1962 but then rendered powerless by the Prime Minister, Milton Obote. In 1966, Obote declared Uganda a republic and himself President. He continued to rule until ousted by Idi Amin in a military coup in 1971.

Obote was reinstated as President in 1980 after Amin was overthrown by a combined force of Ugandan exiles and Tanzanian military. Once in power again, the excesses of

Amin's years in power were ratcheted up as Obote sought revenge on the groups that had supported Amin; mirroring Amin's tyranny over the groups he thought had persecuted people he favoured during Obote's first administration.

A foreign system of socio-political organization imposed on the country led to years of violence and tyranny but Moses and his friends were part of a resistance fighting for a unified country that would incorporate all ethnic groups and end the years of tit-for-tat oppression.

As my relationship with Elisabeth developed so, too, did my friendship with Moses. And as I learned more about his past, the history of his country and the ideals he believed were worth fighting for, I began to play my own role. It felt like a truly righteous struggle in which an oppressed people had been forced to take up arms for their own protection.

As I became more and more involved, Moses' struggle awakened something within me: a dormant echo of my Viking heritage that invoked my warrior spirit. It spoke directly to the codes of honour and principles for which I'd always been willing to fight.

In 1981, responding to widespread civil repression and government corruption, Yoweri Museveni, a former member of Obote's Military Commission, formed the National Resistance Army (NRA) with a small group of supporters. Other underground groups appeared sharing a similar aim and, while some were crushed, others survived in Uganda's bush and rainforests.

While all sought to bring about an end to Obote's rule of terror, many were simply groups of people forced from their homes and villages; survivors of inter-ethnic atrocities and massacres, or of government-backed population-removal strategies that sought to weaken rural support for the rebellion.

The NRA was essentially a dispersed network of small units of rebel fighters involved in the struggle to bring an end to Obote's oppressive regime, maintain their own survival and provide protection to local villages against government troops, foreign mercenaries and state-funded militias of armed thugs. It wasn't a tightly unified force, more a coalition of various factions struggling to survive amidst the confusion created by the vacuum of a weak but oppressive government.

Museveni's dominant strategy was not based on offensive military action, nor on initiating a coup d'état, but on winning the popular support of Uganda's people to the cause of national unity and nationwide peace and security. But as support for Museveni and the NRA increased so, too, had Obote's attempts to destroy opposition through repression and tyranny.

It was as a result of this that Moses had been forced to flee Uganda, now gripped by civil war, and it was in the face of these injustices that I wanted to get involved in my friend's struggle.

Maybe they accepted me because I was Swedish, and because Sweden had never shared the imperialist ambitions of other European countries. My country hadn't been involved in the 19th century 'scramble for Africa', during which other European countries had literally carved up the continent, adding to the West's exploitation and decimation that had started with the Atlantic slave trade.

Maybe they could see that I believed deeply in their struggle or maybe they just thought I was a foolish muzungu with a bleeding heart, but I don't think so. Or maybe they did at first but as time went on, and we developed a trust and camaraderie they became willing to let me use my status as a white man to assist them.

Moses and his friends had a simple wish: to be able to return to a peaceful homeland with their families. To help secure their wish, they were playing their part to make it a reality by supporting people they knew over the border who were directly involved in the armed rebellion.

For the next two years I helped them as best I could. Knowing how to get access to cars with 'Corps Diplomatique' number plates and with my ID that gave me UN status, I assumed the role of 'Transport Manager'. Depending on the job in hand, both proved useful for passing smoothly through checkpoints and roadblocks and ensuring unhindered transport for either goods or people.

Ugandan exiles that supported the rebellion were funding their cause in a variety of ways, some of which were illegal. As a child I'd gone in search of a gang of criminals in a forest close to my home and now I was getting involved with a gang of criminals that perhaps I'd been unconsciously searching for, in a land far from my home.

Even if the authorities would have considered them criminals, I never thought of Moses and his friends as such; their motivation was driven by the will to change their country for the benefit of its people and by an ideology based on community, social progress and the pragmatic need to end oppression before it could irreparably damage their homeland. It felt that theirs was a means to a righteous and just end.

By the time I'd finished school and was due to return to Sweden to go to university, I no longer felt like an outsider in Moses' world but part of their struggle. Going to university wasn't something my parents had been able to do, or theirs, so my going was a big deal for my family.

Fully understanding the value of a good education, Elisabeth, Moses and the friends I'd made on Nairobi's 'other side' wished me well. But I left with a heavy heart. I, too, understood the benefits a university education would bring but I felt as if I'd set out on a path that I had to finish; going back felt like a diversion.

When I got back to Sweden I just couldn't settle. I couldn't get my friends in Nairobi's slum out of my mind. I thought of Moses and his struggle and of Elisabeth and hers. Though very different in their detail, both were essentially struggles for a life better lived. I was in turmoil.

It had been so easy for me to get on a plane and return to a place whose inhabitants barely knew the meaning of the word 'struggle'. My life was so comfortable and easy in comparison; I had choices. It didn't seem right that I should be in Sweden. I felt like I'd deserted my friends and not been true to my commitment to them, so I made up my mind to return to Kenya.

I knew I couldn't tell my parents. They would have been against me leaving university and I respected them too much to be able to hear them say 'no' and then go against their wishes but I was on a train that was already rolling. Making it more difficult was the knowledge of my mother's firm pacifist beliefs. In addition to the idea of me giving up my studies, there was no way she would have felt in the slightest bit comfortable with what I intended to do.

I'd saved up money to help me through university and decided to give it to Elisabeth, to enable her and her family to leave the slum and start a new life on the coast. I also decided that I wanted to go all the way with my commitment to Moses and the Ugandan people's struggle.

EIGHT

I kept checking around myself, as I walked hurriedly down the tarmacked road toward the border crossing and the slum beyond.

Nothing much seemed to have changed during the few months I'd been away, yet it somehow looked different. Everything was familiar but now I was being carried by a sense of purpose that I hadn't felt so strongly when I was there before. Thinking of the first few times I'd walked down the hill filled me with a sense of nostalgia. In some ways, being back felt like a homecoming of sorts.

I hadn't had any contact with my friends since I'd returned to Sweden, but I was confident I'd find them. As I approached the bottom of the hill I slowed my pace. Even though the border between the two universes was a hive of activity, a muzungu in a hurry was bound to attract attention.

I didn't want to cause any kind of stir and I didn't want news of my arrival to precede me. I felt good about being there again; proud that I was following through with my decision. If I'd asked anyone else what they thought, I knew they'd probably think I was an idiot for leaving university and deceiving my parents.

I turned left when the tarmac ran out and proceeded along the street of storefronts. The young woman selling newspapers and candy was still sitting on the slab in front of the Indian man's shop. The man was leaning on his counter. I squeezed his forearm and gave him a 'long-time-no-see' smile before turning to face the back of the woman. I squeezed her shoulder and put a 20-shilling note in her hand. She turned and grabbed my hand. Her face broke into that sunshine smile I'd remembered a few times when I was back in Sweden, as she squeezed my hand with a silent 'welcome'.

A few steps further on, I reached the barely visible sign that indicated my destination. I let my hand brush over the faded letters and went down the steps. Like the first time I'd been there, I stopped in front of the bar's door. I'd changed in the passage of time since then but one thing remained the same; I felt as if I was on the same path that had first led me to the bar.

I slowly pushed the door open and looked into the identity-less, fluorescent-washed room. It was just as I remembered except Elisabeth wasn't sitting in her place with her two friends. On the other side of the room, Moses and his friends were in their usual places below the President's photograph.

My touch on the door had been so gentle it was if I was a ghost on the bar's threshold; nobody noticed me. I could have done the sensible thing and turned and walked back up the steps, returned to Sweden and university, and none of them would have known I'd been there, but I willed myself into the room.

The door closed behind me and everyone turned. I was greeted with a combination of surprise and smiles and then warm words of welcome but as I swept the room with my own smile, Moses' face remained as stone.

The two ladies gave me warm and genuine 'mama' hugs and kisses. They seemed to have filled out a bit since they'd hugged me 'farewell' but they hadn't forgotten our old form of greeting. I was glad old habits die hard and that I kept a hand over the crotch of my trousers because soon enough I felt one of theirs on top of mine. I pinched her nose but our laughter was cut short when I asked where Elisabeth was.

'She died...' was the answer I got.

I was shocked and felt tears well up in my eyes, as my mind flashed back to the times we'd spent sitting side by side, with her chubby hand in mine, under the trees where the slum ended and the Kenyan countryside began; either talking or enjoying a peaceful silence. She had so badly wanted to get out of the slum and return to a natural environment but like so many there, she felt trapped.

We'd sit and look at the world she'd come from but was no longer able to live in. I remember telling her what I think she knew already; that it had always been my world, too. I loved and cherished nature and one day, if I could, I'd make sure she'd return to live in it. Her answer was both poetic and beautiful, with words that spoke in pictures, in a way that is typically African.

'You feel like the shell of the egg I came from, and I know you are real because I have touched your inside.'

I stood in silence in front of the women; listening to my heart absorbing their news, heavy with the knowledge that I'd never see Elisabeth again.

They didn't say how she'd died and I didn't ask. I didn't want to know. Their lives were so precarious that death could come at any time and in any number of ways. It seemed somehow disrespectful to want to pry into the details. I remembered the money I'd intended to give Elisabeth. Giving it to her family would be my way of honouring the special relationship we'd had. I felt devastated.

My greetings to the gravedigger, Moses and his friends were not laced with the same joy I'd felt when I'd stepped into the bar but the feeling that returning was the right thing seemed clearer. As I greeted him, Moses looked at me both sternly and quizzically.

Once we'd all settled down to a round of Tuskers, I told him why I'd returned. He'd guessed as soon as he'd seen me in the bar and was far from pleased that I'd come back; not that he wasn't glad to see me again, he just couldn't understand why I'd want to give up what I had.

I'd anticipated this reaction and could understand how what I was doing seemed to make little sense.

'You think you know why you want to go to Uganda, only you may be wrong.' Moses said after I'd explained why I'd returned.

'What is that supposed to mean?' I wondered.

On one level I knew I was wrong. Little Man's voice inside me had been saying the same thing ever since my feet had touched the tarmac at Jomo Kenyatta International Airport.

Would I be having second thoughts if Elisabeth were still alive? Would I have gone with her instead, to start a new life with the savings I'd brought for her? Suddenly I felt confused, as if I didn't know what I was doing. I told Moses that nobody, including my parents, knew I was back in Nairobi.

'They think I'm at university in Sweden,' I said.

'Yes, that would be their wish. Imagine that, university.' Moses replied, fixing me with his wise and penetrating eyes. 'I remember the years in university in Kampala after independence during the first Obote regime,' he continued.

'We really believed in our government and the future, but we were wrong. And then I was naive enough to believe Amin would make things better. We were many who stood behind him, but I was wrong again. He was a madman and soon we stood against him, too. Now I believe in our National Resistance Army and once again I'm struggling against Obote and maybe I'm still wrong, as I carry on fighting and struggling; still believing it will get better ... But above all I remember my youth, I remember university and my big plans for a bright future...'

I didn't know what to say. He held my eyes with his, as if searching for a clue to the madness he must have thought had taken possession of me.

'I know you're loyal – that won't have changed in the few months you've been away. I'll give you what you need, as a favour-for-a-favour, because you've done so much for us in the time we've known you and that includes all the beer.'

A rare smile crossed his face and I thanked him.

The self-doubt I'd felt evaporated. Moses was going to give me what I wanted; the contacts I needed to find a rebel unit in Uganda. It wasn't going to come with his blessing though; his good wishes, yes, but I could tell he thought I was deluded.

There have been many times since then when I've wondered if I was deluded all those years ago. I was young and idealistic. I wanted to commit myself totally to something I believed, to the extent that I would risk my life for its cause. I wanted to take a stand against a people's victimization and oppression; a situation I felt was morally wrong, and that I was willing to take up arms and fight to put right.

In each moment, we become bound to a version of the future by the choices we make in that moment; writing the script as we go along. At the same time, I felt as if I was on a path that had been laid out before me long ago.

Within a week, Moses had secured the contacts I needed and helped me prepare for my journey to Kenya's western border and into Uganda. Once there, he worked out a route through the bush, along which I'd be met by friends and allies who'd keep me on the right track for my destination – a village in rural south-central Uganda and Alex, an American working with the UN. Moses gave me a coded message to deliver to him.

'Your message is important, it's for our brothers and sisters in the bush but deliver it to the American.' Moses said before I set off for Uganda.

In the months before I'd returned to Sweden, the civil war in Uganda had stepped-up, as more and more people joined the resistance. In retaliation and as a last-ditch attempt, Obote was turning to ever-more violent means to quash the growing rebellion.

Poorly trained and ill-disciplined, the Uganda National Liberation Army (UNLA) were exacting a brutal revenge on villages suspected of helping, or simply thought to be sympathetic to the rebels. In terms of human cost, Obote's repression was surpassing the bloodiest periods of Amin's years in power.

I didn't question my sanity because I felt an overriding conviction that I had a part to play in something which, at the time, seemed to be a simple case of right against wrong. I felt compelled to take the 'just' path and stand on the side of the righteous. But over the two years that followed I was to learn that life is far from simple, its course never even, and that right and wrong are relative and even sometimes interchangeable.

I left for Uganda thinking that black and white were mutually exclusive, but within two years I would be lost in an opaque and insidious grey.

Part 2

ONE

Daylight had begun to push through the dawn mist as the battered Peugeot I was travelling in approached the Kenyan border. As night faded I began to be able to make out the looming silhouette of the Eastern Ugandan highlands in the very near distance. Moses had arranged for a 'friend' to drive me from Nairobi and drop me just over the Ugandan border, where I was to make contact with another 'friend' who would take me on the next leg of my journey.

We'd lost precious time due to a flat tyre and my driver was getting increasingly anxious about having to cross the border in daylight. Though the area we were approaching was a bit of a no-man's land, we had no idea how often it was patrolled by Kenyan border guards.

Once over, I was in but my driver still had to make the return journey.

We'd left the road some kilometres back and were heading through the bush on a well-worn track, obviously not the first people to take that route. My driver skidded to a halt, as the sun was rising behind us; I'd arrived in Uganda. He hurried me out of the car and indicated another track that ran at a tangent to the one we'd driven along.

'Asante sana!' I thanked him and put the remaining 100 or so shillings I had into his hand.

I didn't think I'd need Kenyan money again for a while and had already given most of the money I'd brought from Sweden to Elisabeth's hugely grateful mother, brothers and sisters. Before the week was out, I'd watched them board a bus to the coast in the square behind Burgerland, praying they'd be able to make a life that would make Elisabeth proud.

My driver turned his old Peugeot round and sped off, back the way we'd come. As the car receded into the distance, I was struck by both the silence and the vastness of the landscape I'd been deposited in. After a few years' absence, I was back in the wilderness and it felt good.

The bush began to come to life, as I made my way along the track. In front of me, lush green vegetation swept up into cloud-covered hills. In Nairobi, even at this early time in the morning, the air would already be heating up but here it retained its night-time chill.

As I listened to the caws, cheeps and chirrups of hundreds of birds greeting the day I felt small and alone, as if I were the only human around for miles and miles.

I followed the track for several kilometres before it began to narrow, as my driver had said it would. For the past couple of kilometres or so low-lying bush and scrub had been replaced by taller shrubs and trees. I couldn't see where I was heading but the path was making a slow descent along a steady incline.

I'd been told the track would take me to a river where a man in a boat would be waiting for me; fishing under an overhanging tree on the river bank. The driver had only said it wasn't far, but what's near and what's far means different things to different people.

I could hear wildlife in the trees and bush around me and figured their water source could be close and, sure enough, I was soon able to make out the river glinting through the trees. The path meandered along the river bank. I followed it, keeping a close eye out for the landmark the driver had mentioned and the lone fisherman. The river began to bend and, as it turned, I saw a clump of trees jutting out at an angle on the opposite bank.

A man with a fishing line was sitting in a pirogue in the shade of the trees. I found a spot on the bank just down river from him and casually sat down. I smiled to myself. I was acting as if it was the most normal thing in the world for a blond Swede to be taking a rest after a stroll in the bush, miles from human habitation in equatorial Africa. He'd only have to take one look to know it was me he was waiting for.

I took a long and welcome drink of water from my canteen. The river was no more than 15 metres wide and I guessed the man had already registered me. Sure enough, by the time I'd lowered my canteen, he was paddling over to where I was sitting. He signalled for me to get in his boat, turned its bow and took the pirogue back into the river.

A spare paddle lay on the pirogue's bottom. I picked it up and nodded at the man, he nodded back and I started paddling in time with him. I didn't want to take advantage of his taking me on this leg of my journey and anyway, I've always believed in pulling my weight, whatever the situation.

Very little conversation had passed between the driver and me on the journey from Nairobi, and even less took place on that journey up the river. In a way, it felt unnatural not to strike up a dialogue, but as I'd discovered with Moses, when you're in a particular situation you don't ask questions. You're not there to share each other's life stories. If there's something you need to know you'll soon get told. I'd learned that it was more important to get to know people by what they do and how they do it, rather than how they talk and what they say.

We'd been on the river for at least a couple of hours and I badly needed to take a leak. I turned to the boatman to ask if we could stop, knowing he'd probably tell me to go over the side of the boat, but he was staring intently ahead and sniffing the air, with concern written on his face.

'Smoke from the bush,' he said in Swahili. 'It could be soldiers. Get down. Don't let them see you.'

I'm neither tall nor wide and managed to get myself below the pirogue's sides by lying along its flat bottom. The boatman threw a blanket over me and steered away from the bank where he'd seen the smoke. The reality of the situation I was travelling into suddenly caught up with me.

Like the time when I went looking for the criminals in the forest, I realized this was neither a game nor an innocent adventure. Despite being hidden by the blanket and the sides, I suddenly felt very conspicuous. I could hear shouting and raucous laughter coming from the river bank and through the blanket's thin fabric could see the boatman looking ahead with an expressionless face, while paddling calmly but strongly.

'Hey fisherman,' a man's gruff voice shouted in Swahili from the bank. 'Bring us your catch.'

'Hujambo rafiki?' the boatman shouted back. 'Habari gani?'

I heard the sharp report of an assault rifle being fired and heard the whistle of a round fly over the pirogue followed by uproarious laughter and shouts from the bank. The boatman started paddling furiously.

More shots followed, tearing into the trees on our side of the river. I suddenly felt as vulnerable as I felt conspicuous but, with a skill born of experience, the boatman found a current that carried us swiftly away from the shouts and raucous laughter. When I thought we were out of sight and range I got up from the floor of the boat.

'Bloody bastards,' the boatman said, spitting into the river for emphasis. 'Crazy, drunk and high! You see why we have to fight them?'

This was the reality I was travelling into. I'd been able to control my bladder when the shooting started and I didn't feel like making that stop anymore.

An hour later and the boatman brought the pirogue to the bank. We disembarked and he pushed his boat under the cover of a large bush overhanging the river. The vegetation where we landed was lower and the air felt heavier than in the highlands. We'd left the mountains and trees behind us and I wondered how far we'd travelled along the river.

The boatman led me into the bush away from the river and indicated for me to sit when we reached a clearing. He unwrapped a piece of cloth and gave me some dried fish and bread before taking some for himself. As we ate, he told me to continue in the direction of a tall acacia tree, standing alone in the distance, and then to follow the narrow track that ran by the tree in the direction of the setting sun.

He told me that, if I walked through the night, by daybreak I'd reach a bush track where I could hitch a lift. He warned me to look out for the military and stay hidden if I saw soldiers.

'Me, they'd shoot if I couldn't explain what I was doing in the bush but you're a white man, so they probably wouldn't kill you. But they'd want to know what you're doing here so they'd give you a very hard time.' He said, raising his eyebrows for emphasis.

I thanked him for helping me but he shrugged it off.

'We help each other,' was all he said.

The sun was in its descent, as I set off through the scrub on the next part of my journey. I guessed the boatman would sit it out till well after dark before making his way back up the river and past the soldiers again. I felt humbled by the help he'd given me on my quest. I also felt a little bit uncomfortable knowing that I'd put the man at some risk.

I imagined that people were willing to help because of my involvement with their comrades in Nairobi. I doubted they would have been told the details and wondered what passed through their minds, as they helped a 'crazy' Swedish guy along his way.

As I got closer, I could see the acacia's long shadow imprinted over the tall grass. A gentle breeze moved the grass in waves, sending the tree's shadow rippling like a long, black flag.

By making the decision to come here I was flying my own flag. I was making a statement to myself about what I believed in and what I was willing to do to uphold the principles I valued. Despite how difficult it might be for others to understand why I would do such a thing, in a land so far from my own and for a people who so many Europeans seemed to despise, it made sense to me.

I thought about my father and wondered how he'd felt when he'd been in the Middle East and Congo with the UN, during the 1950s. He'd told me that, during the conflict in the Middle East, he'd been forbidden to get directly involved in the fighting, even if it could have prevented civilian deaths and injury or atrocities against people who happened to be in the wrong place at the wrong time, or who were suspected of supporting the 'wrong' side.

In contrast to being an 'observer' in the Middle East, in the Congo UN troops had taken part in the fighting. I'd often wondered what the hardest thing was for my old man to live with; the demons of frustration that came from a situation in which he'd been forbidden from doing anything to stop the horrors he was witnessing or the demons that came from being directly involved in the horrors of war and party to the human suffering it generated.

Though I didn't know it at the time, it was a question I'd eventually get closer to answering myself.

My night hike along the narrow path brought me to a wider track, criss-crossed by the imprint of tyres in dry, red mud. I realized that I had no idea what direction I should take and also felt quite conspicuous as a lone white man in a land, which after the previous day's encounter with the army, didn't seem a particularly safe place in which to hitchhike.

Despite the tyre marks, it didn't seem like the route would be carrying a great deal of traffic. I sat by the track for a while wondering what I should do before deciding to carry on walking.

By noon, I was finding it hard to keep moving. I was soaked with sweat, my canteen was empty and I was feeling the effects of a sleepless night walking through the bush. The track made a dip and a turn to the left. As I followed it round, in my tired state I almost walked into a Land Rover parked alongside the track. I froze the instant I realized it was there.

My immediate thought was of the army then a middle-aged man with blond hair appeared from the driver's side door.

'Hey! I'm Alex. Looking for me?' He asked in an American accent.

Feeling a wave of relief pass over me, I walked up to him with an outstretched hand and felt it clasped by a firm and confident grip.

'Welcome to Uganda,' Alex said with a warm smile. 'Your journey's nearly over. Come on, jump in.'

He passed me a canteen of water, as I flopped into the passenger seat next to him.

'You're going to be staying at my house for a time, while we sort things out. Have to do it like that, see. It's a tricky situation in this country right now and things take a lot longer to make happen, but you're welcome and it'll be a chance for you to get to know the bush a bit.'

I didn't know what to say. I was feeling a bit the worse for wear but also extremely relieved that I'd actually made it to this point in my quest for the rebels. As we motored along the bumpy track, I fell in and out of a fitful sleep.

I dreamt of the acacia's shadow that I'd walked toward. Like a flag, it seemed to be waving at me but, as I got closer,

I saw that it wasn't waving, it was writhing in agony under a blanket of ferocious ants. I woke with a start. Alex's eyes were firmly on the track ahead. I wondered about the destiny I'd given myself up to.

TWO

Alex lived with his wife in a small village in south-central Uganda. The village started at Alex's house and ended with the village church, with two parallel lines of simple houses facing each other in two neat rows in-between. The houses were either whitewashed or left in the earth-colour of the mud-dung mix they were built from. The roofs were constructed of corrugated metal sheets, palm leaves or a straw-like grass. Some of the houses rested on the ground and others, like my hosts', were elevated. Each had a simple porch at the front.

The village was no more than 60 metres or so long and, in its middle, a tall and imposing teak tree stood like a guardian over the village's inhabitants. Alex introduced me as his guest and I imagined people thought I was a relative of some kind. To be honest, nobody seemed to pay me much attention beyond the warm and personable greetings I was given each day, once people came to recognize me in their midst.

At first, it seemed strange to me that normal life in the village went on from day-to-day. I hadn't really had any expectations about how the war would be impacting the country. I'd certainly had my own firsthand experience on the river when I'd arrived in Uganda but on first impressions, it would have been hard to imagine the village as being in a war zone.

I remember the vibrant sound of the village during the day: of people going about their business, trading, negotiating, building, repairing, talking, laughing and children playing – all against a soundscape of birds, dogs, pigs, chickens, goats, insects and the village donkey.

The men went about in more or less worn clothes and the women in colourful khangas, the textile wraps worn by women throughout East Africa. The village's children wore one or the other depending on their age and gender.

The great teak tree was like a communal centre for the village where people sat in its shade, and where I sat with them on many occasions during my time in the village; watching their faces and listening to their voices, as they shared life's joys and sorrows. And all the while, the children, who cared less about sun and shade in their need to express their joy, played in their carefree and easy way.

War seemed so very far away but, as Alex explained to me, that was how it was; it could seem far away and the next moment was at your front door, and then in your house. It wasn't an urban war being fought in towns and cities but a guerrilla war, with small groups of rebel fighters, many of whom were idealistic young Ugandans tired of years of political oppression and tyranny, who had left their homes, work or studies to fight for a better future.

A lot of the rebels were also people – men, women and children – who'd been displaced from their homes and villages by government forces seeking to eradicate opposition to the corrupt regime.

The persecution and forcible displacement of people perceived as a potential threat didn't start when Milton Obote overthrew Idi Amin. Amin had conducted his own brutal regime of oppression on those he deemed 'subversive', which included individuals, families and, sometimes, entire villages. Obote had followed suit and inadvertently supported Yoweri

Museveni's task to recruit popular support for the NRA's struggle.

Museveni was in it for the long haul, pursuing a slow campaign to win over Uganda's people. Since the war had started he'd given this as much, if not more, importance, as the NRA's armed fight against Obote's military.

Alex knew the reason I'd come to Uganda. He never questioned my motives but Moses and his guerrilla contacts had a clear objective in having me stay with him that went much further than the coded message I'd been entrusted to deliver.

Though I didn't really know it at the time, looking back I can see that, as well as being my point of contact between Moses and the rebels in the bush, Alex also had the role of vetting me. I guess, to see if I was really up to joining a rebel unit. At the time, I didn't really question Alex's role as a member of the UN but looking back I've often wondered if there was actually more to his being in the heart of what was essentially a no-man's land in Uganda in the mid-1980s.

Western power interests had all but washed their hands of direct involvement with Uganda, after Britain and Israel's clandestine scheme to bring Amin to power had backfired on them. But Western power interests would still have wanted to know what was happening on the ground, and how the outcome might impact on their own objectives for post-colonial Africa.

Given that Obote was receiving support from North Korea, the US may have been particularly sensitive to the political situation and I've often wondered if Alex was using his UN status as cover, while actually working for the CIA.

He was a kind and sensitive man, with a gentle and caring wife; far from the stereotype of a covert secret service agent. He'd seen active duty in Vietnam and, at one point during my stay, asked me what I'd known about that war. I answered honestly, saying that I'd been a bit young and too involved in fighting my own fights and sports to take much notice.

I knew he had a son about my age, at least I presumed the photographs that hung on my bedroom walls were of his son, but I never asked. I wondered if he was away studying, like my parents and friends thought I was, or even if he was still alive. Life contains so many tragedies and mysteries, only few of which we'll ever truly understand. The photographs of the boy growing up in Africa will forever be shrouded in mystery, because something stopped me from asking about him. At the time, I figured they'd tell me if they wanted me to know.

Alex also had a daughter. She was a few years younger than my sister and away at school while I was staying with her father and mother. I never met her, though I saw her briefly; that moment was also to become one of the tragic memories I carried from Uganda.

Alex had a small arsenal of weapons. He kept an old Colt .455 revolver wrapped in cloth under the driver's seat of his Land Rover and under the floorboards in his house he kept a single-barrelled Winchester and an old double-barrelled Remington buffalo hunting rifle. The guns looked like they'd been well used but also well maintained. We'd often go into the bush together, sometimes to hunt and sometimes just to track.

Our expeditions also involved a lot of weapons' training. As well as showing me how to use the guns and how to dismantle and clean them, Alex also showed me how to prepare shells using black powder, lead and empty cartridge casings.

On one of these occasions, I noticed movement amongst the lush bush vegetation in the distance. Keeping low, Alex began moving toward it. I presumed it must be some kind of animal. As we got closer, he abruptly switched tack so we were moving in parallel with the subtle disturbances I could see in the near distance.

Suddenly, and just for a moment, I was sure I could make out the camouflaged figures of military personnel in full combat gear.

'Did you see the soldiers?' Alex asked me, as we drove back to the village with our catch of the day; a large warthog for our dinner, and sharing among neighbours once it had been cut up. I told him I had. With expert skill he'd kept us unseen and at a safe distance, moving alongside the soldiers. What seemed most striking was that he'd done it with me as company.

When we arrived home he disappeared in the Land Rover 'to take care of a few matters'. I'd already noticed the vehicle had a shortwave radio under its dashboard, set up for two-way communication. I'm pretty sure that was what he was using to 'take care of a few matters'.

Throughout my stay, there was always something fatherly about Alex's conduct toward me. It seems a bit ironic, given that the majority of fathers probably wouldn't be too keen on their son joining a guerrilla unit but it also left me feeling even more curious about the fate of his own son; if that's who the young man in the photographs was.

I've also wondered since, whether Alex had his own agenda for helping me in my quest to join the rebels. Looking back at the weeks I spent with him it's clear that, at the same time he was checking me out, he was also training me. I've often wondered whether he was preparing to send me in as an 'asset' on the ground and in the thick of things. I'd certainly have been able to provide him with incredibly valuable intelligence.

Whether his prepping me was for the rebels or for his own purpose or both, I never had the chance to find out because my stay with him was unexpectedly cut short. Like so many aspects of my story, unanswerable questions have textured my memories with melancholy and a deep sadness.

On another occasion, when Alex and I were out together, we stopped for a break along a bush track. Suddenly, as if from nowhere, a lone young man, covered from head to foot in dust, appeared in front of us.

Alex didn't seem at all surprised. The man was armed for combat and the way he looked made me think of someone who's expected to be able to manage to survive alone. From the sparse equipment he carried, I could see he wasn't laden down but able to move quickly and with stealth.

The man fitted my image of a guerrilla, as a hand fits a glove. He seemed like someone able to remain away from his base camp for extended periods of time, surviving in and from the bush; someone who would be able to 'do the deed' even where the enemy felt safe.

He carried a Russian AKM assault rifle in his hand very casually, as if they were conjoined. Two belt-like straps tightly crossed his chest, holding a number of ammunition clips and a couple of army-issue aluminium water flasks. A bayonet for his rifle and a machete were also tightly strapped to his body.

'He's a guerrilla and he's been waiting for you!' Little Man's voice piped up inside me.

The 'coincidence' of the young man's sudden appearance freaked me out but it didn't seem to bother Alex and he invited him to join us for food and drink. With a very friendly manner, the man politely accepted and apologized for his appearance.

Before sitting, he took a rag from a pocket, unscrewed one of his flasks, which was filled to the brim and then, as if reluctant to use its contents, finally poured some onto the rag and began wiping the dust and dirt from his hands and face.

'We'll make it silent again. I have water.' Alex said to the man.

'Thank you, Sir.' He replied with a grateful smile.

Alex explained later why the man was concerned about having to deplete his flask; a partially full flask splashes its contents around, creating noise, while a full one remains silent. He told me it was normal for someone operating in the bush to drink their flask dry in one go and then not drink again for the next 24 hours.

The man remained standing in silence when he finished wiping the dust off his face and hands until Alex invited him to sit, which, again very politely and respectfully, he did.

He placed his equipment to one side before joining us on the ground. Along with his AKM, he was carrying a very faded, standard issue, army green backpack with a woollen blanket on top of it, which was rolled-up in a protective hide.

It was all very weird, especially since neither he nor Alex went through even so much as the simplest of introductions. That in itself was very unusual, and made me think that the meeting had been arranged. I knew most Ugandans wouldn't behave like that as polite introductions were considered to be an important part of social etiquette.

At the time, I couldn't figure out if the man was a rebel or an army soldier but I was inclined to think 'rebel'. He seemed so controlled and self-contained and I wondered if that was a sign of his training.

Unlike the soldiers that I'd encountered on my first day in Uganda, he displayed reserve and discipline and didn't seem at all threatening. It felt like there was something temporary about his current role; like he was a very convincing actor who one day would remove his costume and return to his day job.

I wondered why he'd come to meet us and which part of his journey was going to be the longest and the most dangerous – the one he'd made getting here or the one ahead of him? And also what the hell had made him do it? Was he here for me?

I remember feeling quite nervous, almost scared, thinking that perhaps the step I'd taken from Nairobi was about to come to fruition on the ground. I calmed myself with the thought that this man had just happened to be here and that Alex and he had needed to meet.

I couldn't imagine they'd risk the life of a foot soldier, and probably a damn good one by the look of him, for a late lunch with a crazy guy from Sweden.

I hadn't imagined this would be the way I'd make contact with whatever unit Moses and Alex had in mind for me. Rather, I'd seen myself being pointed in the direction of where to find the guerrillas and then being left to it, to manage – or not – through the rambling bush. It was the way I would have preferred it, completing the journey on my own. I thought I would have to prove myself to them and my commitment to their cause first: putting the dot over the 'i' in their eyes and paying a righteous price for the privilege of being there.

But, at that time, I was still so naive about what I would have to pay and had no understanding of what would constitute a 'righteous price' to 'them'.

I'd imagined they'd suddenly pop out of the bush, put a bag over my head and take me with them. At least, that was the good ending. The bad one was that they'd shoot me on sight, or that I'd stumble into the 'bad' guerrillas who'd shoot me on sight.

As we ate together, saying very little, and with me still wondering if the man had come to collect me, it dawned on me that Alex had set this up to confront me with the reality of where I wanted to go; to make me think about what I was doing and where I was heading and to introduce me to one of the people I wanted to risk my life with.

I wondered if this man was part of the unit that had received the message I'd brought from Moses, and if they were simply curious to find out what the messenger looked like. My mind spun around with thoughts and questions as we sat there.

In fact, I would never find out who this man actually was or what those words I'd brought from Nairobi meant to the rebels; if they had meant much at all, or had simply been part of a test or some sort of clearance.

Along the hard track I was to tread, I'd realize that the things I'd done with their brothers in Nairobi had earned me enough curiosity and respect that they accepted my right to be there, maybe with or without Moses's message.

I was aware of the man watching me discreetly while Alex turned the conversation to Nairobi and how I'd arrived in Uganda, but never mentioning my friends in the slum. I began to feel a growing sense of excitement thinking that I was being checked out for my worthiness but it soon become clear that it wasn't to be my time.

After sharing a meal and drinking a couple of beers in the cool shade of a thorn tree, as we were getting ready to go our separate ways Alex produced a camera saying he wanted to take a photo. The man stuck his AKM in the ground on its bayonet in front of us and Alex balanced his Remington against it.

He gave me the photo a few days later; having developed the film in the primitive darkroom he kept at the back of the house. The print was black and white. It showed the friendly young man and me standing and smiling broadly, with bare feet and bare chests toasting the camera with our beer bottles and with our arms around each other's shoulders.

It struck me as strange, and more than a little risky, given the man's probable status as a guerrilla, and the possibility that the army could turn up at any time and demand to search the house, but Alex and his wife insisted I pin the print to the wall of my bedroom.

'One believes what one wants out here,' Alex had said, rather enigmatically, as we drove back to the village in the Land Rover.

'And one doesn't ask the Gods what they don't freely tell you,' I replied.

He laughed at that, as if to say 'you got it boy!'

THREE

I've often wondered what happened to that photograph. It was the last record of me as the 'boy' I essentially still was.

When I imagine the photo, I see myself shrouded in an aura of naivety and innocence. I'd been through numerous adventures with Moses and his friends in Nairobi, but they were nothing compared to what I was walking into now.

If the photo still exists somewhere, it's the only one there is of me at that time; a picture of two young men, one black and one white, captured in time in a seemingly carefree moment but, like all photographs, its two-dimensional surface is just the front for myriad stories it can only hint at.

I can remember lying on my back on my bed, a few days after I'd pinned the picture above the door, daydreaming in the early afternoon

I could hear the tick-ticking of an alarm clock on the small, old hardwood table by the bed and the rhythmic whir and squeak of a fan attached to the wall over the bed. A rustic but efficient-looking bow hung over the table next to a wooden tube that was covered by rough leather. Over the tube's rim, a cluster of cruel-looking iron-tipped arrows poked out.

Looking at the photographs of the boy I assumed was my hosts' son I noticed one showing him standing next to a small elephant. They looked like two buddies in an arm and trunk embrace. Alongside them, a white Catholic priest, most probably a missionary, was standing and smiling.

I was mesmerized by the photos, the clock and the fan; like the captured images, the clock's incessant ticking and the mellow blow and squeak of the fan seemed to hold time in an eternal moment. I felt at home there, the photos reminding me of when I had been a young son – adventurous and never with enough time to live.

The breeze from the fan moved my hair like a caress from the kind hand of my mother. Everything felt good at that moment in the room. The afternoon's light cast itself through the bright, multi-coloured curtains projecting a pattern on to the wooden floorboards. From outside the window, I could hear the familiar sounds of kids playing and adults talking; life in the village was going on in its usual relaxed way.

I was wearing a pair of denim shorts and a clean white T-shirt that my old man had given me that bore the slogan: 'Uganda – The Pearl of Africa'. They were about half the clothes I owned and had been the way I was dressed when I first arrived at the house of my friendly hosts.

Why they'd been so friendly and why they'd risked maintaining contact with the rebels, I had no idea and was never to find out.

My reverie was interrupted by the sound of the diesel engine of Alex's Land Rover, as it came to a halt in front of the porch. I took my last ever look at the photograph of me and the young rebel and got up to join Alex as he got out of the Land Rover.

We greeted each other and he handed me a brown half-litre bottle of beer from a box of provisions on the vehicle's rear seat. He took one for himself, opened them both and we knocked our bottles together.

A white girl I'd not seen in the village before was skipping with a group of girls in the shade of the teak tree. As the rope turned and the girl jumped I noticed she looked a bit like my sister had when we'd first arrived in Africa.

I looked at the church at the end of the village and noticed the priest standing outside its imposing door talking to a little boy and his angelic-looking sister. The priest was mending the boy's homemade, string-and-tin-can toy car. Finished, he handed it back and I heard a faint squeak from the car, as the boy's small running feet followed it from behind, its ingenious steering-wheel extension in his hands. With a ripple of laughter his sister chased after him.

They ran past the red-mud wall of a house, covered in flowers of all the colours of the rainbow, laughing all the while.

Something inside me yearned for the simple, trusting innocence of an unblemished childhood.

The village donkey walked past Alex and me and stopped behind the Land Rover. I started to ask if the donkey ever did anything apart from walk around the village but Alex had turned to look at his wife coming down the steps of the terrace. I could hear her sandaled feet ringing on the wooden steps.

I turned back and saw the girl who looked like my sister jumping the slowly swishing rope and smiling our way.

I started to wave a friendly acknowledgement when a mute detonation tore her and her friends apart.

Almost immediately, another seemingly silent explosion from behind the Land Rover threw me forward and onto the ground. I lifted my head to see something crashing through the corrugated roof of the church at the other end of the village.

A ripping detonation blasted inside its walls, blowing the metal sheets of the roof apart. They rained down like corrugated guillotines, while the church's heavy wooden door flew off its hinges and into the village, as if the 'big bad wolf' had emptied his lungs from inside the church.

I was gripped by the feeling that the skipping girl was my sister and I struggled to lift myself off the ground to go to her aid. The sound of people's panicked screaming burst into my ears, as I limped toward the teak tree.

I passed a group of terrified women, running away from the burning church – some carrying babies and others dragging their children. As they ran past me, a bright phosphorescent flash burst alongside them.

It was the only explosion I remember hearing.

At first, as I slowly came to, I couldn't understand why I had an incredibly strong urge to run. At the same time, I was finding it almost impossible to fill my gasping lungs with air. The memory of the detonations around me and of that last blast, which had thrown the running women and children at me, suddenly fell into my dull consciousness.

As I struggled to breathe, I became aware of a vast silence and a huge weight on top of me.

The first of my senses to return with any semblance of normality was my sense of smell. The final blast had taken most of my hearing and the only eye I could see anything out of was full of grit and running with tears.

Gradually I became aware of touch and taste, as I felt and tasted the dirt the left side of my face was being pushed into. My nails clawed at the compacted surface of what I thought could be my grave.

The foetid smell of blood, faeces and stomach acids from the eviscerated bodies on top of me merged with the acrid fumes from the explosives that had torn the village apart. I struggled not to vomit as I became aware of the putrid stench filling my nostrils.

As awareness seeped back, my initial reflex was to scream for help. I needed to fill my lungs with enough oxygen to cry out, but the left side of my face was being pushed so hard against the ground that my jaws were being forced apart and my teeth embedded into the ground.

I tried to close my mouth but stopped when my teeth chewed even deeper into the dry mud and my bottom lip felt as if it was being torn from my face.

A wave of blind panic washed over me, as my dazed mind clawed for a way to get out of the tomb of mangled bodies. I felt I was climbing death's doorsteps and could see its grim face in my gradual suffocation. My terrified mind told me that if I could make a sign of life it would be enough for someone to become aware of me and help me out: even if it was whoever had been responsible for this – right?

In that pause to question, a chink of light appeared on the surface of my terror and from what was left of my sanity an instinct of reason overcame the will to panic and took a grip on my thinking. Death's face suddenly appeared, as that of whoever was responsible for this horror.

Though it felt incredibly fragile, a wave of calm replaced my panic. I accepted that I might die but I also knew that if I wanted a chance to live I had to appear as if I was dead.

I opened and closed my right eye as fast I could, to try to clear it of the dust and grit that scraped against its lens. As tears washed it clean, my desire to be able to see overrode my pain and discomfort. A blurred impression of light gradually appeared until I could make out the dirt floor and what looked like an adult's chubby leg; torn apart and ending with a splintered bone where a foot should have been.

I fought the waves of nausea with tiny, painful breaths. My lungs were burning but it was all I could manage with the weight of bodies pressing down on me. Light was entering the tomb of twisted bodies from a gap between the mangled limbs, giving me a peephole onto the outside world.

Through the smoke, drifting across the rubble-strewn ground of the lifeless village, I could make out the lower half of a man, in camouflage pants and army boots, carrying an assault rifle. He stopped a few metres away from the mound of bodies covering me. I could feel my heart pumping in my chest and I started gasping for breath, while at the same time not wanting to breathe at all for fear of his being able to hear the life hidden beneath the carnage.

The boots stood there motionless, for what felt like an eternity, as if waiting for me to give myself away. I had no doubt about which side the man belonged to, perhaps because the pants and boots he was wearing bore no resemblance to the clothes worn by the young man I'd met in the bush.

I suddenly thought of Alex and his wife, and of the picture pinned to the wall over the bedroom door. At the thought of the picture my world turned cold and I felt the wave of an unexpected feeling pass over me; not immediate and primitive and fundamentally linked to survival, but crawling and lucid with darkness – guilt.

Had what had happened to the village got anything to do with my being there?

I was pulled back to the reality of my situation by the sight of a woman in a dress, burned to shreds and still smoking, slowly dragging her body into the view afforded by my peephole. She stopped a little way from the boots and turned her head till I could see that, on one side, her face had been burned to a pink and black crisp.

She looked straight into my peephole, as if she knew I was there. I struggled to hold her gaze, not knowing if I was imagining her seeing me but desperately trying to communicate.

She crawled again.

Dragging herself to his boots, she pressed her awful wound against one of the man's legs, as if wanting to smear the man with her horror and suffering.

The man stood stock still, as if the woman wasn't there. Nothing felt real anymore, even the pain I felt seemed to detach itself from my body. I felt a scream well up in my chest but the suffocating weight on top of me stopped it from escaping. I knew this was all very real and that I owed my life to the people whose bodies were pressed down on me.

The woman remained with her face against the boot and leg, and I thought I saw a trickle of saliva run through her white teeth and over her burned lips onto one of the boots.

In the near distance, I could hear the muffled sounds of shouting and sporadic gunshots, followed by an all-out firefight. My thoughts flashed to the guerrilla I'd met in the bush. Had he been in and around the village all along? Who else would have an automatic rifle? Who else would launch a gunfight against the people who'd staged this massacre?

I saw the boot being lifted and the woman's face dropping to the dirt. It came back down on her spine. In the background, I could hear the sounds of a brave and courageous man making a last stand while in foreground a brave and fearless woman was coldly executed.

I wondered if the village had known why I was there. Irrational though it might have been, somehow I felt responsible for what had happened.

Something moved above me. I felt a small knee or elbow jab my numb body and then I heard a little cry; a plaintive whine for help and care.

Through the peephole I saw the executioner's boot step off the woman's back and move to the pile of bodies until it blocked my view. Now, I wanted to fall far deeper into that dark tomb that, just minutes before, I'd wanted to claw my way out of.

I couldn't believe that such a small and helpless cry could attract anything but help, compassion and caring but I was profoundly naive. A small weight started shuffling around among the bodies on top of me and a cold sweat broke out over my entire body. Suddenly, the most painfully guilt-inflicting wish leapt into my mind.

'Let him only see you, little one.'

The killer fired his gun at the baby, silencing its innocent cry with a few grams of cheap metal that passed through its body and lodged itself in my back. Never had I felt more ready than at that moment to die in a struggle for human righteousness; to somehow correct the sinful thought that had welled up in my mind, and appease the crushing guilt it left in its wake.

In an instant, pain took over and I had to struggle against the impulse to move and cry out; knowing that the slightest movement would attract the attention of the killer standing over the pile of bodies and would be the last I made.

I tried to keep everything inside me but it was too much.

I needed to somehow counter the pain that the bullet in my back had unleashed so, praying that I wouldn't be detected, I began to slowly peal my face off the ground.

The intense pain seemed to balance the agony I was feeling in my back. The weight of bodies made it a supreme effort to tear my lip and face from the rough ground but before long I had enough dirt and blood in my mouth to be able to suffocate the cry that had wanted to rush out.

Replacing a cry of pain, words begging forgiveness ran around my skull: 'I'm sorry, little one. I'm sorry, I'm so sorry...' I didn't move again and nothing else did either but I cried silently.

My eyes and face were flooded, while my mouth, open wide against the ground, was as dry from the guilt and shame I felt as the dirt that filled it. When I looked again the boots had gone.

Beyond the well of fear, anguish and remorse that overwhelmed me I saw the body of the woman lying where she'd been shot while beyond her, behind a modest house, giant rotor blades were turning above a straw-clad roof: 'swish... swish... swish...'

Finally the world blacked out. There, waiting for me in the darkness, was the angelic little girl. With divine beauty she began to sing. I'd seen her and her brother before in and around the village but I'm sure I'd never heard her sing.

From somewhere deep within I created the sound of her voice; invoking a beauty so sublime it wasn't part of this world of pain, loss and suffering but of a higher place. She was singing the psalm 'Thou Art a Shield For Me' with a voice that was as flawless as a perfectly cut diamond and as pure as a baby's need for its mother's breast.

It filled the blackness with a calm that I wanted to embrace for eternity.

I've described my memory of the massacre as a linear train of events, in a way that I feel will make most sense. To do this I've had to pick through fractured and disjointed images, and distorted sensory impressions of what I remember from the time. The reality was experienced very differently – everything felt as if it was happening at once and there are memories that seem to make little rational sense.

I have a memory of being in the church moments before the attack took place; floating above the head of a life-sized Jesus carved in wood and nailed to his cross. I remember noticing '1982' carved into the top of the cross above the figure of Jesus and thinking that it hadn't been there for very long.

I remember the church's large door opening and seeing the little girl and boy entering – the same girl and boy who I also remember seeing talking to the priest outside the church in the seconds before the attack. The children sat on the end of a pew in the centre of the church.

As they sat down they turned and gave a shy smile of greeting. I followed the direction of their smile and saw myself, sitting a little further away on the same pew, smiling at the children.

I've got impressions among my memories of seeing Alex and me standing by his Land Rover in front of his house, as if I'm looking at myself from the steps outside the church.

I'm not even sure I could have been standing next to Alex when the village was attacked. The damage to the Land Rover's body was pretty severe, and looked as if it had been caused by grenade fragments. I think I would have been blown to pieces if I'd been standing where some of my memories tell me I had been.

In the intensity of the cataclysm space, time and perspective were somehow warped; leaving my shell-shocked mind with a montage of recollected and fragmented images that I've put together in an attempt to create a lucid account.

After dusk had fallen on the day after the massacre a lone man entered the village.

Although I didn't see him, he would have been camouflaged from head to foot in dried earth and wearing weathered leather army boots and a faded green uniform; the colour of which would have just been distinguishable through the red earth rubbed into it. On his back he would have been carrying a sun-bleached, army-issue backpack and in his hand a Russian AKM assault rifle.

He'd come in search of survivors and clues, perhaps even a 'calling card', left behind by the massacre's perpetrators, and he found me; barely alive but breathing, just. Knowing time wasn't on his side, and after quickly checking to make sure it wasn't booby-trapped, he carefully pulled me out, from under that grisly pile.

With swift and skilled movements, he went to work with his razor-sharp Swiss army knife and removed the bullet from my back. He'd taken one of the three or four boiled-clean handkerchiefs he always carried in airtight plastic bags for cases like this, and used it to plug the hole left by the bullet.

Operation over, and certain that I was the sole survivor, he lifted me over his strong shoulders and set off on the return hike, back to the rebel camp he'd come from.

During the entire length of the night and for the first part of the following morning, as I was carried over the man's shoulders through the bush, laid down during breaks, for him to recuperate and check my wounds, our way of travelling slowly penetrated my delirious and largely unconscious mind.

I've a vague memory of being carried by someone moving at a steady trot, of pain and discomfort but also of an overwhelming feeling that I was being saved.

My saviour's name was Jonathan, the 'Doctor-General' and leader of the guerrilla group for whom my message from Moses had been ultimately intended.

FOUR

As I slowly came back to semi-consciousness, the first thing I became aware of was the sound of muffled voices drifting in and out of my fuzzy awareness. My body felt heavy, the left side of my face raw and my upper back as if a horse had kicked it.

I was lying on my side and, as my vision adjusted to the light, I realized that my hands were together in front of my face, as if I was praying. Sore and swollen, my left eye was pressed into a pillow while my right peered at a green canvas horizon through a gap between my palms.

I was too weak to move but, as awareness trickled back, I gradually began to recall the horror that was unleashed on the village. I remember wondering if I was dead and in some kind of afterlife. I could see a figure a few metres in front of me and, as my eyes began to focus, it hit me that I was in hell.

The figure I could see had the face of demon; horribly disfigured, scarred and contorted. Instead of hands it had claws. It seemed to have stepped right out of the horror of the massacre. Then my mind went into a tailspin, as I remembered the wish I'd made in my will to survive when I'd heard the tiny whine on top of me.

I was convinced I'd been sent to the underworld for that unforgivable thought.

I drifted in and out of a semi-conscious darkness in which I could literally feel a tiny baby's cries tremble on top of me, while being caught in the penetrating gaze of a broken and burnt woman as death took her away.

Whenever I surfaced into consciousness, I was overcome by wave upon wave of self-accusation and doubt; drowning my soul in guilt and shame. Unconsciousness was my only relief from the awful sadness I felt for the villagers and that baby, and from the deep and haunting regret I felt for the words I'd pronounced in my mind in the name of my own security and survival; words that seemed to contradict my deepest principles.

I was tormented by flames that burned me with the question of what kind of human I could be, to wish that a baby would not draw the attention of a murderer toward me? Coupled with this, the feeling there was a possibility that I had been the cause of the massacre left me in a deep, dark, mental well of guilt and recrimination for having survived.

I realized I was still alive but felt no sense of relief or gratitude for my life having been spared, as I tumbled inside thoughts, pictures and memories that coalesced into one bloody mass of a mess. Something made me think I should have known the village was going to be attacked. That somehow I had foreseen it and failed to warn people it was going to happen.

A loop of mental torment, in which I became the perpetrator of the village's destruction, tossed me on waves of dark despair until I was finally beached, back onto the shores of lucid consciousness.

Whether it was a day, or days after I'd first had some awareness of my surroundings, I'm not sure but at some point I realized that the green horizon I could see was actually the wall of a large tent. Still on my side, and still with my hands in front of my face, through the crack between my palms I could see the body of a man sitting up in a rough wooden bed next to me. It was the figure I'd thought was my demon guardian in hell.

Out of my line of vision I could hear a woman's voice, reassuring and filled with humanity and caring, talking to the man. As I began to regain focus, I could see the man's face had been left raw and deformed by the most awful burns. Despite the way he looked there was something about him that radiated a warmth and kindness, as he listened to the woman's gentle voice.

His scarred and twisted hands were cupped and resting on a blanket that covered his lower half. At first my hazy mind couldn't work out why the blanket lay flat on the bed, then I realized the man didn't have any legs. Yet over the collar of his sweater, his twisted face carried a grin that radiated pure happiness. It lifted my spirit instantly.

'It is for you to choose what John is to do with his hands,' the man said in a laboured and croaking voice.

'Open them!' The young woman replied brightly.

The man lifted his hands to reveal a large, colourful butterfly. For a moment it seemed to stagger, as if surprised by the sudden bright light, then it spread its beautifully coloured wings and lifted itself toward freedom. It suddenly dawned on me that I had no idea where I was or who these people were, but I felt safe.

Giving me a fright, the butterfly fluttered past my hands and disappeared. It reappeared again; fluttering between John and me. From behind my hands I followed it until it came to rest in a sunny spot on the tent's canvas, next to a young woman with a dark brown and radiant face.

She was sitting on a stool changing the bandages of the arm of an injured man who was lying on another of the tent's homemade beds. She was dressed in a yellow khanga and a woollen blouse, and she was beautiful.

'Herrejävlar!' Little Man exclaimed inside me.

I could see how the warmth she generated had inspired that look of happiness on John's face.

In my hollow heart I suddenly wanted her to feel something positive about me and it felt very important to me that she did. It didn't have to be the caring I heard in her voice when she spoke to John but something; it suddenly felt incredibly important that there would be something. She must have felt me gazing at her because her attention suddenly shifted to me. She smiled at me but, embarrassed at being caught staring, I shifted my gaze.

'Fool!' Little Man jibed.

I looked back, but too late. She'd stood up and was walking away. Minutes later, she returned with a steaming calabash. She put it on a small, rough table by my bed and sat down on her stool, which she placed by my bed. I was sure she was about the same age as me and I immediately felt she did care for me. As she gently pulled my cover down, being careful not to touch my sandpapered face, I heard someone enter the tent.

A faint 'male' odour, mingled with tobacco and metal, preceded the person. Through the gap between my hands a man's lower body came into view from the chest down. He was dressed in clean but faded green army pants. He carried an AKM in one hand while adeptly rolling a cigarette with the other.

'No smoking in here,' the woman whispered to him.

'Sambana!' the man answered. 'Good morning, my flower child. How is he?'

I felt a spasm of pain in my back, causing me to arch forward. My arms shot forward, striking the table and spilling the fine smelling soup. The man grabbed my flailing arms. 'Slowly, slowly you lucky bastard,' he said, in a mixture of Swahili and English.

'Don't say that,' Sambana reprimanded him, as she picked up the bowl.

I felt mortified that I'd spilled the soup she'd brought me. I was still incredibly dazed and quite groggy but desperately trying to find my way back to some kind of lucidity. The man walked Sambana out of the tent, returned to my bed and sat on the stool. I missed her already and hoped she realized my knocking over the soup had been totally involuntary.

The man tore his roll-up in two, putting one half in the breast pocket of his khaki shirt and lighting the other with a silver Zippo that was dull and scuffed with wear. He pulled on the smoke deliberately, appreciating the tobacco.

'My name's Jonathan,' he said, bluntly. 'It was me who found you, nearly dead, in the village you were staying in.'

The memory of what had happened passed over me like a wave and I found myself struggling inside, as if desperately trying to keep my head above water. I wanted to be able to remember the man sitting in front of me. I thought I recognized him from somewhere but couldn't quite place him.

He spoke English very precisely, with an educated 'Oxbridge' accent. I was sure he wasn't a soldier by trade and wondered what he'd done before the war. I couldn't look at him directly, so kept my eyes on John behind him in the background.

'I knew the family that you were staying with,' he began. 'I'm sure they made you feel at home – they had that habit.' He took a long drag from his smoke. 'Maybe they were much like your own. They're in Kenya, right? Your father drills for water over there, yes? It's a good thing drilling for water – it's like drilling for life,' he said.

I looked at him quizzically. How did he know about my family? I felt like my brain was packed with cotton wool to protect it from the shock of what I'd been through. I noticed the butterfly and turned to it for some kind of distraction. Jonathan must have felt my state of mind. His tone softened.

'I was given the message you brought from our mutual friends in Nairobi. It was important, indeed, and we thank you! You told me on our way here. You told me whether you meant to or not, you were delirious.'

I'd been sure that Alex had passed the message on and if he hadn't, why hadn't he? Hadn't he had the opportunity? Maybe Alex had wanted to set it up so the rebels would have to meet me to get the message. If that was the case, who was the young man we'd met in the bush? Maybe some things happen in the way they do simply because life doesn't allow them to happen any other way. Maybe that's destiny. I felt confused and unsettled.

And what if this guy had been someone else and I'd given them the message? I was horrified at the thought. It must have been written on my face because Jonathan quickly continued: 'Don't worry, you did well. We knew you were looking for us. My friend Alex, your host, told us about you and said you had a message for us. What bothers me is how you came to have friends like those men in Nairobi? I thought kids like you went to fancier places than the slum to have your fun.'

I looked up at the butterfly opening and closing its wings in the sun on the canvas, as if it was drawing in the warm rays in preparation for its next flight.

'Shouldn't you be in school or university, preparing for your future?' He asked me, pulling hard on his roll-up while he waited for my answer. It had gone out so he re-lit it with his worn Zippo.

I remained silent. I didn't have the energy to begin telling him the story that had started way back in my childhood, so he continued.

'Many of my countrymen fear being in their country and try to leave; many are killed trying. Others fear trying and are killed here. You surely know this. But you, you're running the other way – against the stream. What do you think it is that you've just survived?' He shook his head. 'You want to join us? Why would you want to take part in a fight that's not yours?' He sighed in consternation. 'What is it your youth seeks – adventure?'

It was like he was talking to himself, trying to work out the apparent madness of my mission because his questions were coming too fast for me to answer. He clearly had something to say to me though. He said it, leaning closer and almost whispering in my ear.

'This world is grey my friend, not black and white. Take your time to recover then you're on your way. We'll make sure you get back to your family safely.' He leaned back, as if finished, then added: 'What bothers me though is the time and dedication it would have taken to get the trust of our friends in Nairobi. I'm not sure it *is* simply adventure you're after.' He looked at me, puzzled. '*You're* not black and white either, are you?'

Feeling tired and emotionally drained, I turned on my side and closed my eyes.

'I saw my sister and she waved at me,' I murmured. Jonathan pulled down the blanket covering me to check the wound in my back. He seemed pleased with what he found and covered me up again.

'She wasn't your sister, it was my friend's daughter. But don't worry your presence in the village had nothing to do with the attack.'

'What the hell?' I thought. Where had that come from?

How did he know what was going on in my head? It was the biggest and darkest question hanging over me. I was deeply disturbed by the thought that my presence in the village had somehow caused the massacre but, according to this man Jonathan, apparently not. I felt a little relief and drifted into a troubled sleep.

I was in one of 11 rough wooden beds in the 'field hospital', a large army tent, with others who'd either been injured and wounded during the unit's operations, or rescued from villages attacked by government forces or militia. I've no doubt that my mental turmoil expressed itself when I was sleeping in the same way that I heard the tent's other occupants crying out and moaning in their sleep. It was a place of suffering, but also of healing and recovery, where time merged. Its passage marked simply by the light and dark of day and night and the coming and going of more or less pain, both physical and mental.

It was also a place of hope and both John and Sambana exuded incredible positivity. I took great strength from John as I recovered, realizing what he must have been through. From his burns and injuries it seemed amazing that he was still alive. He had such a will to survive and a cheerful grin to go with it. I remember times when I'd hear him croaking, as if possessed by agony, and then when the pain was past he'd be smiling again.

Sambana, as the hospital's nurse, had to deal with human suffering on a daily basis. Yet she did it with genuine caring and selfless warmth that truly humbled me.

As my strength returned and I spent less time drifting in and out of sleep, I began thinking about what Jonathan had said about wanting me to be on my way. I realized that though I'd been involved in helping the cause in Nairobi that wasn't going to underwrite my being able to stay.

More than ever I felt committed to taking a stand in these people's struggle. What may appear crazy with the perspective of years can make perfect sense to someone barely out of their youth and living life for the first time. I didn't care what Jonathan thought about my wasting my future. I just wanted to be there, to fight with them and to give myself to their righteous struggle.

Since I'd been in Nairobi, their struggle had felt familiar; reminding me of my struggles with the bullies when I was a young boy.

I began to hatch a plan that I thought might convince Jonathan to change his mind and let me stay. He'd left me with the impression that he was a hard but just and righteous man, and that he wanted to have nothing to do with my fate if he could help it. Like a sensible grown-up, I think he wanted me out of there and back in school fast.

I knew I'd have to do something important and significant if I was going to stand any chance of changing his mind and I wasn't sure the plan I was hatching possessed that strength.

'You'll have to leave it to destiny,' Little Man said.

I felt as if I was relying on an instinct that told me something would happen to let me stay. I didn't know what, but I knew what I could do to try to get them to keep me, and I could only do my best. Whatever its outcome I had to set my plan into action, as soon as I was recovered enough to leave the tent. Either way, when he visited the hospital on his daily doctor's rounds, I made sure I never raised the issue with Jonathan.

A few days before I was discharged into the world that I could partially see and hear through the tent's canvas filter I was woken by a cool, damp cloth. It was Sambana, wiping the perspiration from my face.

With an effort, I tried to sit up. I really needed to go to the toilet, but felt awkward making that the subject of my first lucid exchange with this lovely woman. I suddenly wondered how my needs and bodily functions had been taken care of up to that point. 'Can you help me?' I asked, struggling to get up.

'I think you should stay where you are,' Sambana said sternly, 'because dead men rest.'

She thought she'd wrapped it up but I replied with: 'Yes, but dead men don't need the toilet, do they?'

'Okay,' she giggled shyly, giving me an arm to heave myself up with. 'It *is* probably about time you started doing it for yourself.'

I could feel her watching me as I hobbled off in the direction of the hospital's latrine.

FIVE

During my final two days in the hospital I persuaded Sambana to let me do some light exercises. It felt good to be able to move freely again but I was very weak. The closest I'd ever come to feeling so totally worn down was after being incredibly sick with meningitis in my early teens. I knew I'd have to build up my stamina before putting my plan into action.

The hospital tent was set a little way away from the camp's main area so I'd been unable to build up much of an impression whenever I left the tent to go to the toilet and I was very curious about the camp. On the day of my discharge I decided to take an early morning walk to acclimatize myself.

Spread out and hidden under trees and among the vegetation, the camp consisted of huts and shelters made with bush material and canvas tents in various shades of green. In the early morning breaklight I could make out figures, protected from the chilly, dew-laden dawn in sweaters, coats or blankets, preparing for the new day.

I could see men in faded green uniforms stretching and yawning and others, who looked like they'd been awake all night, sitting in pairs and small groups by modest campfires. There were women tending to small cooking fires and children of all ages slowly emerging into the dawn.

Though most of the camp's inhabitants seemed to have already been up before first light, a few bodies were still resting in hammocks or on simple beds raised off the ground on short poles to keep them away from potential dangers that might be crawling there.

As I walked along what felt like the camp's central path, I became aware of a rhythmic pounding. Rather than hearing it, I could feel it in the ground under my bare feet. I followed the vibrations to a group of men exercising under a circle of trees. Either in bare feet, in car-tyre sandals, rubber boots or leather army boots, the men exercised in unison. Every now and then, they stamped the ground in tight rhythm.

It felt like a village concealed in the bush. It was a home: to refugees and survivors; people displaced and dispossessed by the violence and conflict; people, younger and older, who had joined the fight for their freedom from the oppression that was squeezing the life out of their country. From orphaned children and teenagers to former army personnel and militia members who'd defected to the other side, and from city folk to country people who, through choice or circumstance, were living an almost subsistence existence on the war's front line.

I was struck by how resolute and tough these people were; particularly those who had been living in this way since the early days of the war, or even before Obote came to power, as a result of Amin's targeted oppression. The reality of the circumstances that significant numbers of Uganda's people had been forced into, either directly or indirectly, hit me.

It was one thing hearing stories and accounts of how the war was impacting on the country's people, but now I was experiencing it for myself.

I was later to hear how hundreds of thousands of people in rural areas had been forced to leave their homes and villages, and made to live in camps in order to de-populate areas that the government feared would support the NRA. The camps were under military control and the people in them subject to brutality, privation, rape, intimidation and every abuse of human rights under the sun.

Rather than limiting support for the NRA these policies actually increased popular support, which in turn led to more government-backed violence and repression.

I was sure about one thing, the people waking up around me weren't living the bush lifestyle because they wanted to. I could see that life here was basic and hard. Brought down to earth fairly and squarely, I returned to the hospital to say my farewells and prepare myself to enter the world of the camp, and hopefully implement a plan that would enable me to stay in it for a lot longer than Jonathan had in mind.

As I thanked Sambana for her care and fine cooking, which I assured her had more than anything else brought me back to health, I felt an unexpected pang of regret at having to leave. Rather clumsily, I told her that I hoped I'd see her again. She smiled politely and gave me her best wishes for my continuing recovery.

John and I exchanged a warm hug. I told him how his spirit and inner joy had been a light for me as I'd slowly made my recovery and that I looked forward to seeing him up and about outside the tent. He laughed a full-hearted, croaking laughter.

'Ndio bwana, my wheels will meet your feet on the track.'

He'd been working on the designs for a wooden wheelchair. He meticulously refined his intricate diagrams by carefully holding a stubby pencil with what was left of his right fingers and hand. I didn't think to ask him at the time but, looking back and remembering his drawings, they were so finely executed I'm convinced he must have been a draughtsman before the conflict caught up with him.

I once again felt very small and humbled as I left the tent with John and Sambana's blessings.

I found a spot under a huge jacaranda tree and sat down with my back against its sturdy trunk: its broad boughs shading me from the already hot rays of the morning sun. I wasn't quite sure what was next. I'd passed the tree on my walk earlier that morning. It felt like it might be at the centre of the camp and a good place from which to contemplate my immediate future. I didn't know how quickly Jonathan was going to try to organize my departure but I figured it might well be in the next few days, so I didn't have long.

The sun played through the surrounding trees' foliage, casting a kaleidoscope of shapes over the motley settlement. Motes of dust sparkled in the air, while soft trails of smoke drifted lazily upward and people quietly went about the business of their day.

Set under the shadows of the branches and leaves overhead, and among lower-lying shrubs and bushes at ground level, the camp looked like mutant vegetation that had grown up from the forest floor.

Though I wasn't that well acquainted with the African bush, years of roaming my native forests had given me what felt like a harmonic attachment to the wilderness. It never felt strange and scary; whether native or foreign, lit by day or hidden by night. On the contrary, it felt familiar and like my 'home' environment. Strangely, I'd felt a similar way in the environment of the slum: a different kind of wilderness. I didn't feel at all out of place in the camp's environment.

Amidst the lush greenery in front of me a group of men were playing cards, using old ammunition boxes as seats and a table. Though they kept their voices low, snatches of their tribal dialect occasionally reached me over the 20 metres or so that separated us.

I smiled as they reached the end of their hand and the winner raised his arms in victory.

One of the players, who I noticed had lost a leg, must have felt me staring. When our eyes met I suddenly felt like an intruder. The sharp look on his face seemed to say: 'What gives you the right to stare and what are you even doing here, you shoeless bastard?'

The thought made me look at my feet. I'd left the worn, car-tyre sandals I'd arrived in on Jonathan's back under the bed in the tent.

Back in Kenya I'd been told that being without shoes was a sure sign of poverty and shoes were the first thing people would buy if they came into money. Maybe I was projecting my own insecurities but at the time the man's look seemed to be asking how a white man could be so poor as to be without shoes, and what was he doing there anyway. I turned my almost-healed face away from the card players.

A few metres away from me, and also under the shade of the tree's rich purple blossom, a small and peculiar-looking man with closely cropped hair sat dragging the blade of an *assegai* (a long-bladed spear) against the blade of a long, and lethal-looking, vintage Prussian bayonet-saw. He didn't respond to my gaze but continued his precise, slow movements.

He was wearing a wine-red tunica and an AK assault rifle lay on the ground next to him. As if completely oblivious to my presence, he checked the sharpness of the blade, casually spat on it and continued.

Above and around us, the air was filled with the sound of hundreds of birds singing to the forest: chirping and chattering to one another. My attention was distracted by the sounds of children's voices coming from a neighbouring tree.

Three boys were in its branches, taunting a girl as she walked along the path toward them. The youngest of the boys, who I guessed to be about five years old, was clothed in nothing except an oversized, torn and dirty T-shirt. He stood on a fat branch next to a boy of about eight who was wearing an old pair of boxer shorts and a tent-like army shirt without sleeves and with three round holes in its back. I wondered who its previous owner had been and if the holes really were the bullet holes they looked like.

Sitting on a wooden platform above them was a boy of about seven, laughing cheekily at the oldest boy's taunts. He was wearing a bleached T-shirt and old cut-down denim jeans. One of his eyes was covered with a leather patch but from his other radiated mischief and glee in equal measure.

Speaking a mixture of Swahili and English, their taunts were getting more and more personal as the girl got closer. All of a sudden the boy on the platform, who'd turned in my direction, hushed his friends and indicated up the path beyond where I was sitting. Their cheeky demeanour suddenly switched to sensible and I turned in the direction of their sober gaze. Jonathan and Sambana were approaching.

The girl looked up at her tormenters and gave them a mocking look. As she walked past the jacaranda tree, she noticed me sitting under it. Such was her surprise at seeing me, and so full-on and brazen her stare that she walked smack-bang into Sambana coming down the path in the opposite direction.

Sambana gave the girl a mock-stern look while telling her it was rude to stare. Embarrassed, the girl giggled nervously and hung her head. The three boys, now standing on the path at the foot of the tree laughed derisorily until Jonathan shot them a withering glance. They immediately stiffened and like lightning brought their right hands to their foreheads in a salute.

Without softening his look, Jonathan nodded for them to 'stand at ease'.

'Make yourselves useful,' he said, sternly. 'See if any of the mothers need water fetching.'

'Yes sir, Doctor-General, sir' the boys piped in unison before heading off into the bush.

The girl turned on her heels and ran after them, but not before Sambana had given her a sisterly hug and a reassuring smile.

I stood up as Jonathan approached me. We shook hands and he indicated for me to sit back down before joining me cross-legged on the ground. Meanwhile, Sambana was greeting the peculiar-looking small man who'd been sharpening his blades. Putting her forehead and nose against his, they looked into each other's eyes.

'I see you, Pole,' she said.

'I see you, too, Sambana,' the man replied. 'But long time no see.'

They gave each other a warm hug. He dropped back down to the ground, clapping the ground next to him in a signal for her to sit.

Jonathan uncorked the calabash jug he'd brought with him and offered it to me, as three very curious men passed by. I took it, unsure of its contents. I was tempted to take a sniff, or at least ask, but thought it might seem discourteous.

A familiar aroma greeted me as I lifted it to my mouth and tilted my head back, while following the look of the three passing men. They saluted Jonathan in mid-step and turned their gaze elsewhere, as I felt the warm, bitter taste of whisky in my mouth. I wondered if Jonathan had spread the word about the background to my presence in the camp. There must have been people in the hospital tent who'd seen me brought in. I couldn't believe they hadn't asked questions.

The whisky felt warm and pleasant in my chest. I passed the jug back to Jonathan.

The man Sambana had called Pole leaned toward Jonathan and indicated toward me. He spoke to Jonathan in a dialect I hadn't heard before.

'Pole, Lucky,' Jonathan said, looking from the man to me, then looking from me to the man, 'Lucky, Pole.'

'Come again?' I asked. 'Is that what you're calling me?'

The whole village had been wiped out and I'd been given a nickname by which to remember the experience. I was totally shocked. I couldn't believe what Jonathan had just called me. I think he could tell but it didn't seem to bother him.

'You're a damn lucky bastard, my friend, and you should never forget that.' He replied.

I didn't know what to say. He was right. For all sorts of reasons I probably shouldn't have been there but I was, and it was what I'd wanted. I now just had to see if I could get to stay.

It took me a long time to accept the name Jonathan had given me.

Most of the people I got to know in the camp didn't use the names they'd had on the 'outside world'. It was as if each of the camp's individuals had left their former 'self' behind to join the struggle on its front line. Names located people. They identified your ethnicity, the region you came from and your likely allegiances: either real or 'by association'. Having a bush name erased those frames of reference and levelled the field.

Exploited by the colonial administration, inter-ethnic conflict had underpinned much of the brutality and oppression meted out and suffered during Uganda's colonial past, and in its post-colonial present. In an attempt to counter this, the NRA's driving ideology was based on a country united across tribal and ethnic divisions in which people would be known by their individual merit, not by the ethnic group or clan to which they belonged.

I felt lightheaded from the whisky and found myself looking at Sambana who was gazing at the doves in the blossom overhead. Almost as soon as my eyes had fallen on her she turned her dreamy gaze toward me.

'Herrejävlar!' I heard Little Man exclaim.

For a moment I felt myself falling into her brown-so-dark-they-looked-black eyes. I quickly pulled myself back and smiled, almost embarrassed. When she smiled back, I felt a glow warmer than the finest whisky.

SIX

Through metre-tall, yellow grass, Pole moved low: cutting a path under a crescent moon with his short, sinewy body. Suddenly he stopped; frozen, like a cat with its senses peeled before it pounces. A few metres away and travelling alongside, I pulled up sharply. I couldn't see Pole through the thick grass but I'd been able to hear and feel his progress in the grass's gentle swishing.

For a moment that hung on a gossamer thread, the crickets fell silent. In my mind, I pictured Pole in his red tunica, his bayonet-saw in its sheath on his back, magazine belts strapped across his chest and his AKM at the ready. A hand reached out through the grass and touched me before I knew it was there.

I kept as still as Pole. Even if he hadn't told me, it seemed to be the way to behave. Childhood memories of tracking animals in the forest flooded my mind. I was dressed in my denim shorts and 'Uganda – The Pearl of Africa' T-shirt and, following Jonathan's instructions, was covered from head-to-foot in red-brown earth, like the guerrilla I'd met with Alex.

A seemingly disembodied hand tapped me twice on the shoulder before receding into the dense grass. Very cautiously I advanced, the grass softly stroking my face and body until in front of me I could detect the dark silhouette of a building against a barely lit, night sky.

I'd had a single, cryptic instruction from Pole, as we'd covered the distance from the camp to the village through the bush:

'Be still, follow hand.'

Throughout the journey I'd felt as if I'd kept the tempo of our progress slow and that had he been alone, Pole would have moved with a speed I couldn't begin to imagine. The irony of his bush name dawned on me; 'pole' is Swahili for 'slowly'.

As we got closer to the building its shape began to look increasingly familiar. We were behind the house where I had stayed with Alex and his wife. The memory of what had happened in the village hit me like a kick in the stomach and on an impulse I stood up. With no regard for the situation and in a daze, I walked toward the house. Pole must have been watching and probably wondering what the hell he was doing babysitting an idiot.

As I turned the corner of the house, I saw Alex's Land Rover leaning on its side in front of the house's torn-up terrace. A terrible stench made me catch my breath and I covered my nose and mouth with my T-shirt. The rank, sickly smell was coming from the village donkey, which was lodged under the Land Rover and propping up its side.

A flashback to the massacre that had torn the village apart burst through my mind. Fragmented memories started clawing, dragging and pulling at my senses from a dark and lonely place.

The nightmare had been real.

Since waking up in the hospital tent, my disturbed and shell-shocked mind had been struggling to come to terms with the feeling of being in the middle of several worlds at the same time. Revisiting the setting of my nightmare, I suddenly felt as if these worlds were collapsing in on me; my disjointed memories collided with the realization that I was in the place where the horror had taken place.

In my mind, the plan I'd come up with to get Jonathan to let me stay seemed to resemble a reality with which I could connect. I forced myself to focus on it and somehow managed to put myself on autopilot, though feeling as if I was moving through a dreamscape.

I climbed in through the Land Rover's blown-out windscreen, reached under the driver's seat and pulled out a textile wrap. I felt the comfortable weight of the Colt .455 revolver in its holster in my hand, wrapped up in the cloth.

'This housi where you belonging? Pole whispered spookily through the blown windscreen.

Startled, I nearly jumped through the roof. Our eyes locked for a second and for the first time I caught a look in his eye I'd see again; this man was from a place that I'd always felt existed but was far from all I knew. I clambered out and laid the gun on the ground next to the Land Rover's front wheel.

Checking the general state of the vehicle, I wiped its mud-covered CD-plate and, with my T-shirt wrapped around my face to lessen the overpowering stench, got my back under its tipped side. Without needing any prompting, Pole got his wiry frame next to mine and we heaved and heaved till we had the Land Rover's four wheels back on level ground.

With the Land Rover upright, I picked my way around the broken boards of the house's terrace and into the hallway. Knowing what I was doing was for the cause I knew Alex had supported made me feel that I wasn't violating his home and that he wouldn't mind me taking what I had gone there for.

I got on my knees on the hall's parquet floor and began lifting it, as I'd seen Alex do each time we'd gone hunting or tracking. Reaching into the dark space under the flooring with my fingers, I found what I was looking for.

I lifted out two long objects rolled up in woollen covers, four heavy shoeboxes and a military-style shoulder bag. Looking over my shoulder I saw the half-opened door to the room I'd stayed in. I crawled over to it on my knees and stopped outside.

Under the bed, I could see the canvas shoulder bag containing the few things I'd brought with me from Sweden. I felt my skin prickle uncomfortably as I glanced into the room. From then to now, in the time it took to live through and recover from a massacre, I wondered what the hell I was doing and felt suddenly overcome by the feelings of guilt that had consumed me as I recovered in the hospital tent.

I was hit by a wave of sadness and had to catch myself as I began to feel myself start to fall. I reached under the bed and pulled out the bag.

I'd told Jonathan I'd wanted to go back to the village to pay my respects and to say my 'farewell'. Reluctantly he had agreed to let me go with Pole as my guide. He told me that people from neighbouring villages had buried the massacre's victims in the hillside cemetery next to the village.

Once Alex's arsenal was in the Land Rover I asked Pole to wait while I climbed the low hill a little way beyond the village. Pole was itching to get going and I knew I couldn't take long to pay my last respects, but it was something I had to do. On the horizon, dull shafts of light were encroaching on the night sky's velvet blackness.

It was one of Africa's arrestingly spectacular dawns, when the bride of the moon – the sun – reaches out for her groom; who is waiting for her in that only moment they will ever share. Even before she was near to appearing, the light of her presence was warming and soft, as his was sleepy, yet reassuring – telling his bride that he had kept her safe in the dark, and that she could now shine without fear.

As I sat on the hill's summit the sun started to rise, sending light streaming through the trees edging the hill's eastern side, while the crescent moon cast its glow over the slumbering grass on the hill's western bank.

Marking the final resting place of the victims of the massacre, crude wooden crosses, and small mounds of stones, threw long shadows over the hill's slope and the morning dew that shrouded them.

I shivered in the dawn's chill, as the memories of what had taken place overcame me. Tears welled up in my eyes and I let them fall freely to mingle with the bitter soil of this burial ground as I gave in to grief.

But my grief was accompanied by those feelings of guilt that had tormented me during my darkest moments in the hospital tent. Had I been the cause of the massacre? Had my friends in Nairobi been arrested, tortured and forced to talk? Had the village been targeted because of Alex's presence there?

The rustic crosses and stones, tragic reminders of the village's inhabitants – of Alex, his wife and his daughter – begged the question: why me? How was it that I was the sole survivor? How was it just, in the scheme of things, that these kind and lovely people may have died because of me? That Alex's daughter had returned to the village on the day of the massacre made the tragedy even deeper. Was this what I had chosen to become a part of?

'Where exactly do you think you're going?' Little Man asked me, almost echoing what Moses had said on my return to the slum.

I wasn't sure. I felt like I'd been successful in realizing my plan to retrieve Alex's guns and Land Rover. I thought Jonathan's unit would be able to put them to use, and hopefully they would encourage him to let me stay, but I didn't know where this path was going to take me. It's precisely because we can't foresee the consequences of our choices that life can often feel random.

I was on a course that I had to see through; going in deeper on a path I couldn't seem to step off. I wondered what exactly I'd been spared for.

Pole was more than ready to leave when I returned from the cemetery. We'd probably only been there for 35 minutes in total, but that was 30 minutes longer than Pole would have liked.

Before we set off I changed into a pair of green combats that had been in my canvas bag and rinsed the red earth out of my T-shirt, putting it back on to dry on my body. Wanting him to look like a Westernized African, I managed to persuade a reluctant Pole to put on a pair of jeans and a T-shirt but he refused to go as far as shoes. I told him if we got stopped I'd say we were UN workers.

Though the Land Rover's windows were all blown out and the driver's side looked like a lunar surface, its engine seemed okay and it didn't take much to get it started. With me driving, and Pole telling me where to go, we set off along a bush road back to the camp. Pole had put the Winchester, his AKM, ammunition and bayonet-saw on the floor of the foot well in front of the passenger seat; covering them with his red tunica.

We stowed the shoeboxes and shoulder bag under our seats but Pole had kept the Remington close to hand, under a blanket on his lap. As we set off, Pole took the Remington out from under the blanket, broke it open and closed it when he saw it was loaded and then started gesticulating.

'In bush, big calibre gun good, nothing make bullet go lefti-righti. Like hammer – BOOM!' Pole exclaimed, before spitting a huge gob of chewing tobacco juice out of the window.

I put the Colt .455 under my right thigh, remembering my father telling me how he'd always kept a pistol to hand when driving through hotspots in the Far East and Africa.

There was nothing about Pole's demeanour that suggested he felt in the slightest bit nervous or fearful. As for me, I was deeply anxious. I really didn't want to have an encounter with the army. Even if the rulebooks said they weren't authorized to search UN-marked vehicles, or harass UN personnel, Jonathan had warned me that those rules were no longer valid in the current situation.

Things had got so bad that the laws and rules people had once adhered to were now being ignored. What made it worse was the fact that Obote's ailing government hadn't paid large numbers of soldiers for months and some, figuring they still had to make a living, had started to run their own pirate crews.

We drove past giraffes eating from the green crowns of trees in the bush along the track. As we went by, the bouncing vehicle scared them into a lilting gallop; the voice of Nat King Cole, coming from a cassette player bolted to the Land Rover's bulkhead, accompanying their graceful escape.

'Natti Kingi Coli – good stuff!' Pole had said, with his thumb in the air and a look of glee on his face when he'd rummaged through the contents of the glove compartment and found the tape.

Already incredibly intrigued by this very unusual man, I couldn't resist asking him where he was from. His voice sounded like he was mimicking someone when he answered: 'Me from around here, there and every fucking where – father Matabele, mother San.'

I guessed the language I'd heard Pole and Jonathan speaking must have been Matabele. I knew it wasn't the language of the San, as that was characterized by distinctive tongue clicking sounds. It made sense. From Zimbabwe, the Matabele were ferocious warriors while the San were renowned for their hunting, tracking and survival skills.

I looked at Pole. His complexion was much lighter than Jonathan and Sambana's and his kindly looking face was beginning to wrinkle. Something about him made me think he was probably older than he looked. Though looking like he could be in his forties, he was probably more likely in his late fifties.

It dawned on me that Pole was an outsider, too, and I felt drawn to something about him. He was by far the coolest guy I'd ever met, but not at all in the Western sense of the word. There was something about him that exuded a wisdom and confidence that I'd never before come across.

I'd heard about the San, or 'bushmen', as white people commonly called them.

They were one of the few traditional hunter-gatherer peoples left on the planet, and certainly one of the oldest cultures. It's thought they originally came from Tanzania, and then over a period of centuries moved south and west, from Zimbabwe to Botswana and the Kalahari Desert. Possibly as a result of war and persecution from aggressive tribes moving into land they occupied.

They're still a persecuted people and, because of their traditional ways of life, they're perceived as being 'primitive' and 'backward'. The reality is quite the opposite. Having learned how to live in harmony with some of the most hostile environments in Africa, they're a profoundly wise and hugely accomplished people. It's just that their accomplishments aren't measured in the same way most of the world now measures cultural achievement; in technologies that cause waste and destruction and in lives enslaved to global financial markets.

Nat King Cole had given way to Dire Straits when Pole's mood changed: his natural warmth suddenly disappearing, to be replaced with an icy cold edge. It was incredibly unsettling and at first I couldn't tell why. Then I noticed a black bicycle lying on its side by the track. A few metres further on, a male corpse lay on the ground; its head crooked to one side, its face planted in the ground and four bullet holes in its back.

We stopped.

I took the revolver from under my thigh and checked to reassure myself it was loaded. I felt my heart start to beat faster and again asked myself if this was what I had come for, but it was too late for cold feet. I turned to Pole expecting him to tell me what to do. Jonathan's final words, as we'd left the camp, that we should remain unseen and avoid engaging with the military at all costs, rang in my ears.

'They go, but maybe not far. We drive on.' Pole said, with a subtle hint of eager anticipation in his voice.

He was right they hadn't gone far.

SEVEN

I cautiously manoeuvred our vehicle around a long curve bordered by dense vegetation. As we rounded the curve in the track a camouflage-painted Land Rover came into view, parked in the shade of the trees about 50 metres ahead of us.

Hearing our approach, three soldiers in green, government-issue uniforms stepped onto the track. Their AKs were pointing straight at us. I glanced at Pole, who was surveying the scene ahead intently. He shot me a look, blinked one eye and pointed to himself, as if to say: 'Follow my lead.'

The sense of fear I'd felt when we'd seen the murdered cyclist was suddenly replaced by a feeling of anger, bordering on rage, and the desire to seek revenge.

I remembered the pain and humiliation I'd felt getting bullied as a child, and the rage that had consumed me at the injustice of being victimized. I thought of the innocent victims of the massacre, of Alex and all the other people in the village, and felt a fury spreading through my body, as we drew closer to the soldiers.

The three soldiers surrounded our Land Rover as soon as we stopped; two soldiers on Pole's side and one on mine. The one on my side eyed the damaged vehicle suspiciously, only acknowledging my presence with the rifle he kept pointing directly at me.

Keeping my eyes locked on him, my hand grabbed the revolver under my thigh. I could hear the other soldiers talking to Pole in mocking tones. They were using fear and intimidation as their first line of assault. It sounded like they were well practised. I thought of the dead cyclist, and of other innocent and unarmed people on whom they'd probably fed their twisted sense of power.

They were like vampire hyenas, relishing our situation. I had to work hard to keep my feeling of rage at bay and follow Pole's example of total calm.

The soldier moved closer to the Land Rover. An odour of stale sweat, alcohol and tobacco permeated the air around him. He looked at me coldly, with absent and bloodshot eyes. I realized the fact we were driving a UN vehicle probably carried little weight with him.

'Get out!' He barked.

Both his manner and accent were rough. I had the feeling it was their intention to play with us before the killing started. In the instant it took to digest this, my fear returned. If I were to die at the hands of this man, this stinking hyena, what would have been the point of my being born? I wasn't sure I'd win if the encounter became a fight between life and death.

My mind went into overdrive, as I started to think of ways to get us out of the situation peacefully without anyone getting hurt.

'As you can see from the vehicle's plates, I'm a diplomat working with the United Nations. You know very well that you have no authority to order us out.' I said, as authoritatively as I could. 'Here are my papers.' I added, handing him the ID that had been in the canvas bag under the bed in Alex's house.

He looked at my outstretched hand clutching the papers with disdain, making no attempt to take them.

'Hey boss, give me your T-shirt.' One of the soldiers on Pole's side shouted roughly at me. I ignored him.

The soldier closest to me was peering into the back of our vehicle, casually checking the seats. Finished with that, he took the ID that I was holding out to him, but not before trying to peer into the front of the Land Rover. I kept my body forward, partly leaning on the steering wheel and partly on the door, doing my best to block his view of the front interior.

While he went through a charade of pretending to study my ID, I noticed a Liverpool FC sticker on the butt of his rifle. Maybe I could divert him into a conversation about football. Ironically, Liverpool was my favourite English team. I thought I saw an opening and then he asked me for Pole's ID.

'He's just started working for me. His papers are being processed in Kampala.' I said, quickly looking over at Pole.

He was smiling subordinately at the two soldiers, as if scared, while they continued to mock him.

'Whisky? Cigarra?' One of them demanded. 'Good music. You give me.'

I suddenly noticed Dire Straits were still playing. Pole turned up the cassette player and the two soldiers began dancing, while aggressively jabbing the air with their rifles toward Pole.

'You!' The soldier on my side barked at Pole. 'Get out.'

'Listen,' I countered. 'He's a member of the UN's staff, working for me. You have no authority.'

'No ID, no UN.' The soldier replied. 'You go, he stay.'

There was a wad of rolled-up notes in one of the shoeboxes we'd brought from Alex's house. Maybe we could buy our way out. My mind was racing, as I tried to work out how I could get to the money, knowing that any attempt would only draw attention to the weapons and ammunition we'd stowed away.

I started trying to remonstrate with the soldier but could feel the ground slipping from under me when suddenly an almighty 'BOOM!' exploded next to me. My head started to turn toward Pole before coming to a halt as the thought: 'You won't be able to turn back fast enough,' shot through my mind.

Out of the corner of my eye I saw one of the two soldiers on Pole's side hanging backward in space, with both his feet off the ground. I shot my attention back to the soldier on my side.

Shock was registering in his eyes but he'd shifted his grip on the AK and its barrel was swinging in an upward arc. The revolver was in my hand and out from under my thigh before I knew it. Eyes bulging with adrenaline, I fired through the Land Rover's door.

Almost simultaneously, a second explosion rent the air as Pole fired the Remington's second barrel; this time at the other soldier. Thought became obsolete as instinct took over and I emptied the revolver into the soldier on my side. He staggered backward, wildly firing his AK as he fell.

My head turned back round to Pole. The second slug from the Remington had hit the third soldier in the shoulder, virtually tearing his arm off and flinging him backward. His face, which moments earlier had projected callous mockery, now had terror etched across it. Spun off balance he hit the ground next to his friend, as blood pumped from a ruptured artery. What happened next was totally unexpected.

Pole leapt from the Land Rover with a harsh, guttural sound rising from his throat. He fell on the soldier with the severed arm, still alive and squealing on the ground, and silenced him with one stroke from his bayonet-saw.

With his back to me, sitting astride the dead soldiers and framed by the Land Rover's open passenger door, I could see Pole moving like a crazed being from another world, first over one soldier's head, then the other's. Finished, he stood and turned to face me; two bloodied tongues in his hand.

'They talking shit no more.' He said, before throwing the severed tongues at the soldiers' mutilated corpses.

My head was in a spin. I was pumped with adrenaline and in a state of complete shock.

Pole got back into the passenger seat. He was covered in blood and grinning from ear to ear. It was a moment I'll never, ever forget. It felt totally unreal yet, with my senses heightened beyond the extreme, super-real at the same time.

If Pole drenching himself in blood was my proxy baptism, it was also the moment that the curtain concealing the animal from the man was rent in two. If I'd had foresight, would I have chosen the path I'd taken; along which I would learn the best and the worst about myself and our human species – things we try to deny and pretend are otherwise?

EIGHT

In the few minutes at the roadblock, I learned that in extreme situations when your life is in jeopardy, particularly during the intensity of a firefight, you don't ask how, when and why, you just act. It was a lesson I forgot, with tragic consequences, the next time I was in a similar situation.

Pole was in total command from the moment that he decided to confront the soldiers and I followed his countdown. Just like that, we went from talking and my trying to negotiate a peaceful way through, to killing.

When it had come to it, there was never any question – it was them or us. Killing the soldier was an act of personal survival. If I hadn't killed him, he would have killed me.

I'd never seen myself as a 'killer'. I'd never killed anything other than fish to eat before, and I'd felt good about that. I didn't take the act of killing, or of hurting other people, at all lightly and I had no desire to be in the situation where I'd have to kill, but I also knew what war entailed.

Following the incident, I didn't feel any sense of regret; it felt like self-defence but I knew I'd crossed a line that I'd never be able to step back over. Though the soldier had seemed like a symbol of the evil I'd gone to Uganda to fight, he was also a victim of that same evil.

Now I know that war only serves to perpetuate evil but back then I thought the struggle necessitated its own violence; it was justified.

It was all so much bigger than anything I'd ever been a part of before and I went where it took me. I hadn't been through any kind of military training that had broken me down in order to build me back up again – conditioned to kill.

I went into the situation thinking I'd be able to stick to the moral of 'only if I have to', stay out of trouble, as far as possible, and assist how I could without getting involved in killing. Once in the situation, however, I couldn't make those kinds of choices. It would have been a luxury and, in the extreme nature of the situation, totally untenable.

I can't, nor will I ever, judge Pole. I have no terms by which to do that. We came from very, very different backgrounds, culturally; and the references I might use to assess him would bear no relation to how he might assess himself. Pole became my brother in the bush and my mentor, and I'll never, ever forget him. The man was an enigma par excellence and I will always carry him with me in my heart. Ultimately it was Pole, or at least his phantom, that showed me the way toward redemption, after I'd become lost in a grey netherworld.

Taking Pole at face value, it would have been easy to think he was simple, even a bit of a simpleton, but beneath the surface he was possessed of a deep and timeless wisdom. He had no interest in trying to impress people and absolutely no concern whatsoever about what people might think of him.

He was totally at ease with who he was and, though he'd had a remarkable life, I never once heard him speak about himself in relation to his past. It was as if the present was all that mattered; he was, quite literally, 'a man of the moment'. Everything I learned about him was picked up in dribs and drabs from the few people who knew him and, each time someone recounted a tale or anecdote, it simply added to his mystery.

Pole was brought up by his mother's family and schooled in the ancient traditions of the San. At some point in his life he'd been press ganged into scouting for the South African Special Forces.

I was told an apocryphal story of how, in Namibia, he purposely led a Special Forces unit into an enemy ambush and then 'disappeared'. Later he turned up in Botswana, where he met Jonathan.

Whether it was true or not I've no idea, and I never mentioned it to him, but he did meet Jonathan in Botswana and, having experienced the feats he was capable of, where Pole was concerned it wasn't beyond the bounds of possibility. He was the gentlest man I've ever met. He was like the ripples on the surface of a lake brushed by a soft breeze under warm summer sunshine or like a stream flowing over and around anything that lies in its path. Yet, like water in a storm or a river in full flood, he could be just as deadly.

Once we were driving again, after the roadblock, we travelled in silence. Pole seemed to know some minor tracks that were barely visible and for much of the journey the 4-wheel drive came into its own as we drove off-road. Finally Pole tapped me on the shoulder, indicating that I should slow down.

He pointed to a tall and voluminous bush. I drove up to it and pulled to a halt but he told me to continue into the foliage. It was like a bush garage, as if created to park inside.

I turned off the engine and waited for instructions but Pole had already gathered together his gear and was out of the door.

He discarded the Western clothes he was wearing, put back on his tunica and was kitted-up and ready to go, while I struggled embarrassingly to strap the Remington and my canvas kit bag on my back, and an ammunition belt around my waist.

We left what we'd brought from the house, and the guns

and ammunition we'd taken from the soldiers on the track, under a blanket in the Land Rover and set off at a steady jog. I had no idea why we weren't driving all the way back but figured there was a good reason so didn't ask.

I tried to keep up with Pole but after an hour my energy began to flag. Without comment, and with sensitivity to my tiredness, Pole slowed the pace. Several hours later and surrounded by darkness, his hand came up indicating for me to stop. For some while the terrain had become increasingly forest-like, making progress for me more difficult and I'd taken more than one tumble.

Cupping his hand in front of his face, Pole began making the sound of a bullfrog in a steady and repetitive pattern. Within a few moments, an answering call came back through the trees. With me following behind, he walked on, while keeping up his call at regular intervals.

Back among the tents and shelters of the guerrillas' camp, Pole told me to go to the shelter Jonathan had assigned me. It was a crude wooden cubicle, no more than two and half metres long and a metre and a half wide, housing a rickety old military camp bed and a couple of wooden crates for seats or for storage.

I unstrapped the rifle, my bag and the ammunition belt, and put them on the camp bed.

Cocooned in the hut's gloomy darkness, I sat on one of the crates and pulled off my car-tyre sandals. My feet were sore and blistered. It felt good to be back in the camp but I had no idea if I was staying. By going back to the village, I'd wanted to show Jonathan that I had something to offer, that I wouldn't be a burden and could usefully contribute to the struggle. I didn't know if it would be enough, but at least he'd agreed to the mission.

Something landed on the ground beside me, waking me from my reverie. I reached down and felt a gnarled, old pair of leather army boots. Looking up, I saw Jonathan's silhouette framed in the hut's doorway.

'For me?' I asked, hopefully.

He didn't answer and I sensed his mood was sombre. Having for an instant thought the boots were a symbol of being accepted, I wondered if I was about to get my marching orders and the boots were for my walk out of there.

'Against my better judgement I said you could go. You needed someone to show you the way so I gave you my best man and I also gave you strict orders that you weren't to be seen or get into any kind of confrontation.' He said sternly and rapidly.

'We got caught out.' I said feebly.

'Dirty hyenas on us before we know.' Pole's voice chipped-in from the darkness behind Jonathan's shoulder.

'I told you; nobody was to see you, hear you or even bloody smell you.' Jonathan was furious. 'If you can't follow a simple order what's the point?' He railed, projecting his final words at me.

As he was speaking, I picked up the boots and, turning them upside down, began hitting them, one-by-one, against the ground. In the gloom of the hut's interior, I saw the dark shape of a large spider drop out of one of them and go into a defensive posture; pointing its front legs up and out. Knowing how aggressive the little buggers could be, and how quickly they could move or even jump, I crushed it before it could get any ideas.

I couldn't believe it had been a coincidence. Even though it was always worth checking, it didn't happen *that* often to find a bloody Hulk of a spider in your shoes.

'Friend of yours?' I asked Jonathan, without expecting an answer. As anticipated, he didn't give me one.

Pole stuck his head into the hut. I winked at him but he just stared blankly back at me. It was clear I wasn't going to get between these two. Their loyalty to each other was rocklike. It was the kind of loyalty you could only earn through much time and shared hardship. I wondered if I'd survive long enough to earn it from them myself.

'Him just baby,' Pole said. 'Even me baby once. We see body of man on bicycle they kill. I want to kill them. Hyenas no see, no speaki now.'

'Good on you friendi,' I thought.

Shaking his head, Jonathan turned and marched off.

Pole had been upfront and honest about what had happened. The fact that he'd wilfully taken us to the roadblock, when we could have easily headed off cross-country, just made me more convinced that he was the most remarkable person I'd ever met.

Before disappearing into the dark, Pole tossed a small cloth bag at me.

'Baboon arse, good.' He said slapping his thigh. 'You eat.' I thanked him and reached into the bag for a slice of dried bush meat.

'At least someone cares,' I thought.

I had no idea if the boots were a welcome or a send-off. One thing was for sure though, my feet were so blistered it was going to be a while before I'd be able to get them on. Wanting to avoid my feet becoming infected and knowing that the slightest cut could easily turn septic, I decided to go to the hospital the next day and have Sambana look at them. Then again, I thought, she might think I was being soft. I remembered the way she was and realized that it probably wouldn't even cross her mind.

Sambana hadn't crossed my mind since Pole and I had left the camp, and her sudden presence in my thoughts came with a warm feeling. I lay on the squeaky old camp bed and pulled a cover over me. I was quite looking forward to seeing her again.

NINE

I limped into the hospital tent the following morning on sore swollen feet. John's face lit up as soon as he saw me and likewise, for me too, seeing him again brought a really good feeling.

'Hu jambo, bwana,' I said, giving him a greeting hug.

The bed I'd vacated was still empty so I sat on it and we chatted like old friends. When I showed him my feet he characteristically used them to turn his personal situation into a positive, commenting on blistered feet being one less problem he'd ever have to deal with in the future.

As we were talking, his attention suddenly shifted to a spot behind me and I saw his face light up even more than it had when I'd stepped into the tent. I turned, and immediately understood his rapture.

Wrapped in a deep-blue and flame-red khanga, with freshly braided hair reaching to her shoulders and a vivid smile illuminating her dark and flawless complexion, Sambana entered the tent, looking more like a princess than a nurse. I turned back to John and made my eyes go wide like saucers. He laughed.

'She is a single lady, you know.' He said with a wink.

'I'm not in her league, man, look at me.' I replied, indicating my unkempt and rough-looking appearance.

It was true, I felt like a mess. Even under the camp's conditions, Sambana looked like a true lady while I must have looked like a tramp. I suddenly felt awkward and self-conscious. I wished I'd made more of an effort to tidy myself up before coming to the tent. Thankfully there'd been a clean T-shirt in the bag I'd brought back from Alex's house and, with Sambana already making her way toward us, it was too late for me to hide.

She greeted us in her characteristically warm and friendly fashion, following which John proceeded to tell her about my feet and their desperate need for some TLC. It was like he was playing matchmaker, making me feel even more uncomfortable.

As for Sambana, she just went right along with John's game. I got the feeling she knew I was squirming and was having fun winding me up.

Of course, though there was no way I was going to admit it to myself at the time, TLC from Sambana was exactly what I wanted. It just wasn't what I'd come to Uganda for.

'It's the hospital's Outpatients' Clinic you need,' she said finally, when they'd finished teasing me.

She told me to wait in a chair under a large mango tree behind the hospital tent.

'Is that the waiting room or the actual operating theatre?' I asked with a smile.

'That's our private treatment centre, only the best for our guests,' she replied.

The familiarity I'd felt seeing John again had made me feel like I was part of some kind of extended family, but Sambana's comment brought me back down to earth – I was still just a guest. Within days, Jonathan might have me out of there and heading back to Nairobi.

I waited for Sambana in the cool shade under the tree's canopy, watching a female monkey tending her young in its branches and listening to a glorious symphony of birds all around me. If I did have to leave there was much I would miss and much of that I was just discovering.

Carrying a large aluminium bowl, Sambana joined me under the tree. She told me to put my feet into the bowl, explaining that the warm liquid contained an infusion of bark and herbs with antiseptic properties.

'It's not easy getting medical supplies out here,' she said. 'But thankfully we always have our bush medicine.'

I was about to ask her how long she'd been in the camp and initiate a conversation when she excused herself and disappeared back into the tent. I was crestfallen.

'What *are* you thinking?' Little Man asked emphatically.

He was right. What was I doing entertaining fantasies of romance in the middle of a guerrilla war? Then Sambana reappeared carrying a chair, which she placed close to mine.

'That's more comfortable,' she said, sitting down. 'Now we can have a chat.'

In an instant my crest had risen again, and to hell with Little Man and his thoughts on the matter. I wanted to get to know this woman.

If you've ever been in the company of someone you hardly know yet feel as if you've known all your life and with whom conversation seems to flow effortlessly, like a bubbling spring, you'll know how I felt sitting in the mango tree's shade under the spell of Sambana's brown-so-dark-they-looked-black eyes. To be honest, I can't really remember what we talked about.

I know I told her a bit about me, and how I'd come to be there, and she told me the same about herself, but for the three or more hours that we sat there together what I remember most is the feeling she exuded. When I'd been in the hospital tent I'd heard Jonathan call her 'flower child'; and she was a child of flowers.

I remembered the field I used to walk through to get to the big forest near our first home in Sweden. Being with Sambana felt like being in that field of summer blossom. All at once, she was the rainbow-coloured flowers and the sunshine's nurturing light, the field's vast expanse and the Earth's firm embrace. All at once, time stood still and hours passed in a moment.

When Jonathan came to find Sambana in the 'Outpatients' Clinic', pointed in that direction by John, he did a double take when he saw us wrapped up in each other's conversation. By then, having absorbed most of the infusion, my feet had turned into giant, spongy walnuts.

'Well, that should sort your feet out,' Sambana said; noticing Jonathan and bringing herself back to earth.

'I messed them up on the mission to get the Land Rover,' I explained to him.

'It's true; he's going to need to rest them for a couple of weeks before he's ready to go on any more long hikes.' Sambana added.

Jonathan looked at us both suspiciously, suspecting a conspiracy. If there was one, it had been totally spontaneous.

'I've got someone I'd like to introduce you to, when you're ready,' Jonathan said to me.

Then turning to Sambana: 'And could I have a private word inside the tent,' finishing with a raised eyebrow; 'when you're ready.'

Jonathan went back inside and Sambana took a large square cloth, sat cross-legged by the bowl in front of me and spread the cloth on her lap.

'Give me your feet,' she demanded, looking up at me and patting the cloth. 'I hope you're not going to leave us any time soon, I enjoyed our chat,' she said politely but rather curtly; as if the field of summer blossom had been a figment of my imagination and our relationship had always been strictly that of nurse and patient.

Except I wasn't sure they taught you to dry feet in nursing academy, especially the way she was drying mine.

I was speechless. She'd taken me to a place I'd never ever been to before and suddenly she was Sambana the nurse, while I was still lost somewhere in space. She could weave a powerful magic and I was definitely under her spell. She lifted my feet off her lap and gently placed them on the ground.

'Thank you,' I said, sincerely.

'You're very welcome,' she replied, standing up, placing the folded cloth over her forearm then picking up the bowl.

While I sat dazed, glued to the chair under the mango tree, Sambana walked slowly and majestically toward the hospital tent; her hips swaying like a pendulum below her slim waist and her ample African behind rolling in rhythm. She turned back to me when she reached the tent's opening flap.

'Yes, I am looking at you,' I thought, as our eyes met, 'and this time I'm *not* going to look away.'

TEN

I waited for Jonathan on the path in front of the hospital and we started walking slowly back into the camp.

'Did you know Sambana's my niece?' He asked, and I replied that I did.

Sambana had told me under the mango tree. She'd explained how, toward the end of Amin's dictatorship, suspected of being an enclave of opposition, her family's village had been attacked by government-backed militia. Sambana had been at boarding school when the atrocity took place but the rest of her immediate family were all murdered. Fifteen at the time, she was advised to stay at school for safety.

The country was descending into turmoil as Amin went to violent lengths to maintain his powerbase. He'd significantly increased the size of the military, but with little or no training or discipline whole units were operating outside government control: resorting to banditry and terrorizing rural populations. Within weeks, Sambana's school was attacked and she fled.

Like scores of other children and teenagers orphaned as a result of atrocities, Sambana had sought protection by locating and joining one of the insurgent groups of 'good' guerrillas operating in the bush.

She'd tried to get a letter to her father's brother, Jonathan, who, after studying medicine in the UK, had been working as a doctor in Kenya. Her letter took some time to find its way to him. By then, he was working in a field hospital in Botswana, tending to casualties of the various conflicts taking place in neighbouring countries at that time.

By the time Jonathan received Sambana's letter, Amin had fled into exile and his successor Milton Obote was instituting his own repressive regime. Jonathan returned to Uganda, taken there cross-country and through the bush by Pole.

'So, she told you our family history.' He stopped and turned to me, his voice becoming heavy with emotion. 'I don't think you realize the tragedy of the situation you've walked into... what we Ugandans have been through.'

Sweeping his arms around at the trees surrounding the camp then pulling at the strap holding his AKM across his back, he continued bitterly. 'None of us would have chosen to live like this.' He gave me a penetrating look. 'That's why I don't understand you at all.'

I held his gaze. 'You're right, it isn't my fight, but I believe in what you're fighting for and I want to make a stand for what I feel is right,' I said with conviction. 'I can look after myself and I'm not a stranger to this.' I continued, looking at the trees. 'If you really want me to leave I wouldn't want to stay but if there's a part I can play, I will.'

Jonathan looked at the canopy above us. Shafts of incandescent light were bursting through the foliage in a celestial laser show; projected by the midday sun.

'Maybe there is,' he said thoughtfully, looking back at me. 'Maybe there is.' He turned and, as we continued walking along the path, took out his Zippo and lit a torn-in-half roll-up.

'My niece likes you... crazy girl.' He said.

'She's obviously got good taste.' I replied, tongue-in-cheek.

Ignoring my attempt to humour him, Jonathan continued, 'I'm like a father to her, you know. I inherited the responsibility when my brother was murdered and I take it very seriously. Sambana's all I've got.'

I wondered where this was going.

'She wants me to let you stay,' he said.

I stopped abruptly, completely taken by surprise.

'She's invited you to dinner this evening and she asked me to give you the directions to her hut,' he said, studying my face for a reaction. 'Like I said, I didn't choose any of this. Soon after I found Sambana, the leader of the group she was with was killed. As the most educated person connected to the unit I inherited his role. I'm not a killer, I'm a doctor but we Ugandans have had enough of what's been happening to our country.' He looked me straight in the eyes. 'I'd be a killer for Sambana though, and don't forget that.'

I knew what he was saying but wasn't quite sure of the full implications. It felt like a shotgun wedding of sorts, but since there was absolutely no need for a shotgun to get me to dinner I guessed it was just Jonathan's tacit warning that I behave like an absolute gentleman. I was so in awe of his niece I wouldn't have entertained the idea of behaving in any other way but I hadn't bargained on this.

Everything had taken a sudden and totally unexpected turn, but it seemed to be where the flow was going, and I wasn't going to resist.

Jonathan led me along a path and into an area of the camp I hadn't seen before. It felt like it was on the camp's outer perimeter: diagonally opposite, and on the other side of the camp from the hospital tent. There was a little more space between the trees, and fewer tents and shelters.

Sitting on a couple of ammunition boxes outside a wooden hut, and using a larger ammunition box as a table, two boys in green, oil-smeared army shorts were cleaning and oiling the working parts of two of the rifles we'd taken from the Land Rover at the roadblock.

The boys, who couldn't have been older than 12 or 13, stood up and saluted when they saw Jonathan. He returned their salute, indicated for them to sit and, looking from one to the other, introduced us.

'Moto, Baridi, this is Lucky. It was him and Pole that hijacked the fresh guns and ammo.'

The boys looked at me, and I smiled and nodded. Looking at them more closely I thought they seemed older than I'd first thought. They nodded back at me without smiling.

I saw the Liverpool FC AK leaning by the hut's open door. Through the door I could see dark green ammunition boxes of various sizes below shelves lined with an assortment of weaponry. I guessed this was the camp's arsenal. Most of it probably having been obtained in the same way as the weapons Pole and I had brought back. Taking weapons from fallen enemy was purely practical and had nothing to do with trophy collecting; that – and raiding government arms' stores – was the only way the rebels could arm themselves.

I asked Jonathan if I could have the AK with the Liverpool FC sticker. The boys hadn't checked it over, cleaned and oiled it, so he said we'd pick it up on our way back.

'Come on, I've got someone I want you to meet,' he said, nodding at the boys and continuing along the path.

Through the forest's vegetation a 10-by-15-metre camouflage net came into view. Rising three metres or so from the ground, it was stretched between the surrounding trees in a clearing off the path. As we got closer, I began to be able to make out the unmistakable sounds of Peter Tosh's Mama Africa coming from the clearing. Jonathan led me off the path toward the net.

In its shade I could see the Land Rover that Pole and I had rescued from the village. A blue light flashed intermittently beneath its jacked-up front, which looked like it was coming from a welding torch. Sure enough, as we reached the vehicle, a man in a pair of goggles stood up on its far side. He pulled them off his head; revealing a friendly-looking, aquiline face framed by thick, shoulder length dreadlocks.

'Lucky, Heile. Heile, Lucky,' Jonathan introduced us.

Heile wiped the oil and grease from his hands with a cloth and sat down on the Land Rover's bonnet, before giving me a firm handshake.

Discovering that Heile was from Ethiopia made me feel even less like the odd-one-out, or maybe Jonathan was making a point of introducing me to all the outsiders in the camp. Either way, it made me realize that I wasn't totally unique in signing up for the struggle as a non-Ugandan.

'Maybe you'll always feel like an outsider,' Heile later said to me, during one of our many heart-to-heart conversations. 'Just get used to it. Don't let it bother you so much.'

I liked Heile immediately and not just because of his choice in music. I didn't pick up any feelings of hostility from him. On the contrary, he just seemed to accept my being there without question.

'You believe in what the people here are fighting for and you've chosen to make it your fight. That's a good enough reason for being here.'

He was always full of humour and a bloody good laugh, and was forever taking off on mind-spins about theology and sociology, history and psychology. He was a man who seemed to love pots where people mingled and melted. He was an ear, too, when no one else had the strength to listen, and without ever having to be asked.

Heile explained he'd driven the Land Rover back from the bush garage and was now carrying out repairs on its chassis, most likely damaged during the attack on the village.

There were a number of vehicles under the net, including

another Land Rover, a pick-up truck and a battered Volkswagen Beetle. Looking like he was in his thirties, a mechanic by trade and a guerrilla by conviction, I think Heile had an inkling of what had driven me to seek out the rebels.

As soon as Heile heard I'd been invited for dinner with Sambana he reached into the back of the Land Rover and brought out the battery-operated cassette player that had been playing Peter Tosh.

'You've got to have music if you're romancing a lady,' he said with a twinkle in his eye, handing me the cassette player and a couple of tapes. 'Just don't use rewind or fast-forward, it kills the batteries.'

Openhearted, laid-back and friendly is the way I'd describe my first impressions of Heile. He was also obviously far more romantically experienced than I was. As well as the music, he suggested I take some wine to my dinner date. When I looked at him askew, wondering where he thought I was going to get a bottle of wine from in the middle of the jungle, he told Jonathan to take me to Mama Palma Vini. I looked at him, bemused.

We left Heile working on the Land Rover and walked back up the path to the weapons' store.

'I may take you on our next mission – if you're still with us,' Jonathan said, as we retraced our steps along the path. 'That is – if your feet are sufficiently recovered.' The barely disguised sarcasm was carried perfectly by his posh English accent.

Remarkably, I'd hardly noticed my feet. Sambana's infusion had worked miracles but then again I was still walking on air. We collected the AK and one of the shoeboxes I'd brought back from Alex's house, and proceeded back to the camp's 'residential area' and Mama Palma Vini's.

Located in the second of the camp's dukas and run by a plump woman in her fifties, Mama Palma Vini's was the equivalent of the local pub and sold alcohol, brewed behind the duka.

She looked me up and down when Jonathan told her I was after a calabash of her liquor. I got the feeling she wasn't sure if I'd be able to handle it. I'm not a tall guy and was probably still a bit on the skinny side after being hospitalized, but then she didn't know about my professional drinking exploits, not that I had plans to initiate Sambana into the dubious practice.

The big mama eyed me like a wise judge as she handed me a medium-sized calabash, warning me not to drink its contents all at once.

ELEVEN

Suitably clean, and wearing my best old clothes, I made my way along a small path bordered with friendly, thorn-free, bushes. Just as Jonathan had said, the sound of a steadily flowing river soon reached my ears.

There are moments in life when everything seems to be absolutely and perfectly in place, like being in the snipa on the pine-framed lake in Sweden with my daughters: priceless moments existing outside the onslaught of time's relentless passage. Walking along that path, I felt everything fall into place. It was a strange and profound feeling. It was as if my life up till then had been leading me to this precise moment on this very path, and that somewhere, deep down, I'd known it was going to be so.

The path led to a natural platform set in a clearing on the river's west bank, about 200 metres from the camp's closest 'homestead'. The platform offered a vantage point over the river's calmly swirling waters below and across the river to the opposite bank, which was bordered by lush bushes and myriad trees. About 60 or so metres away, on a flat 'beach' on the opposite bank, I could see a couple of long Nile crocodiles soaking up the last rays of the day's sun.

On my side of the river, a flame tree in full bloom rose up from the clearing floor, the late afternoon's sun turning its orange blossom fluorescent. Under its vivid canopy, an iron pot hung over a small fire in front of a long, fat log. A cosy-looking hut, topped with green canvas and set back against the vegetation, completed the scene.

I wondered where Sambana was. The pot was gently simmering so I guessed she hadn't gone far. I took Heile's cassette player and the calabash from my kit bag and placed them on the log. Against it, I leaned the AK and a metre-long jacaranda branch I'd cut from a tree on my way there, laden with strongly scented purple blossom.

I freed my still slightly swollen feet from my sandals, sat down in front of the log and, as I waited for her, breathed in the peaceful feeling that surrounded Sambana's corner of the camp.

After a while, she appeared, slightly out of breath from the effort of climbing the bank from the river below. Hanging on her back from a leather strap across her chest, the barrel of an assault rifle pointed upward behind one of her shoulders. A cloth bag was tied to a fishing rod that she carried over her other shoulder.

I wasn't sure if she'd seen me so I turned my attention to the fire to give her time to get her breath back and re-arrange her khanga after the steep climb up the bank. Looking at the fire, my feelings for Sambana hit me like Thor's hammer.

I felt a profound, complete, pure and absolute love that I'd never known or even imagined existed. Though later I felt a bit stupid thinking this had actually happened it was as if at that exact moment the forest's frogs, crickets and birds slowly and simultaneously began their musical preparation for the sunset.

I guess it wasn't impossible, as they always began their chorus at precisely the same time every evening. Maybe it was just the first time I'd noticed their glorious symphony, as they heralded the arrival of this heavenly beauty. I looked up and smiled. Sambana smiled back at me. I think we both felt a little shy but there was no sense of awkwardness or discomfort.

'Greetings, Lucky,' she said. 'Your arrival warms my heart.'

She looked gorgeous. Her face was kind, her eyes deeply intelligent and strong, her skin soft, dark and shiny, and her youthful body toned and shapely.

'It's my pleasure,' I blurted out, 'my arrival is my pleasure.'

'Good one, my man!' Little Man commented sarcastically.

I didn't care. I was happy – just bubbling with joy. I stood up, not sure what to do next and then I remembered my gifts. 'Don't come any closer.' I said. Understandably, Sambana looked surprised. 'Close your eyes.' I told her.

Her neck was long and slim, her cheekbones high and pronounced, and her forehead straight and proud.

The image of her standing there covering her eyes, the fishing rod with the cloth bundle over one shoulder and leaning a little into one hip so her khanga was pulled tightly around her athletic curves, will stay with me forever. The moment she allows me to touch her, I thought, I'm not going to be able to keep my hands off her and the fact is, from the moment she did, I couldn't.

Her fine and slender bare feet were speckled with red earth. I thought it made them look even prettier. To me she was the perfect, simple, solid and sweet girl that, in the deepest corner of my heart, I had always wished I could meet. And there she was in front of me with a light brown palm, outlined by milk chocolate-brown skin, covering her eyes.

I noticed the AK on her back. I'd intended to give her the Liverpool FC gun but then thought about how I'd come to own it and figured it really wasn't that appropriate a gift for a pretty young lady, so I left it where it was. Instead, I picked up my other 'gift' – the branch of perfumed jacaranda blossom.

'Which hand?' I asked. Keeping her eyes tightly shut, she pointed.

'Right!' She exclaimed.

'Wrong hand!' I replied.

'Errrrm, left then!'

I quietly walked forward, stopped in front of her and brought the blossom up toward her face. Her nose twitched, as she caught the sweet scent of jacaranda and she broke into a radiant smile. I couldn't help but imagine how the full, soft flesh of her purple-red lips would feel against mine.

'Open your eyes!' I said.

I thought she'd guessed what was under her nose; its fragrance had filled the air around us, adding to the sense that I'd entered a corner of paradise. But when she opened her eyes and saw the branch in front of her face, she jumped back in surprise then burst into a bubbling peel of laughter. I started laughing too.

I felt this huge sense of relief, as if I'd arrived at the place I was meant to be with the person I was meant to be with, and with our whole lives ahead of us.

'Thank you very, very much,' she said finally, still giggling. Taking the rather large branch from my hand, she gave me a little peck on the cheek and skipped over to the log. 'Come and see what I've caught for our dinner.'

She unwrapped two fat fishes from the cloth that had been tied to the rod, laid them on a broad, oiled stone by the fire, then stirred the vegetables cooking in the pot over the fire. I suddenly remembered the wine.

'I nearly forgot,' I said, handing her the calabash.

Smiling, she unstoppered it and sniffed its contents.

'From Mama Palma Vini?' She asked.

'The one and only,' I replied.

'We're all refugees here, Lucky – refugees and survivors, all of us – you, too.'

I felt a sadness in her voice that I wanted to take away. I didn't want the beauty of this moment to become tarnished with the tragedies that lay behind the lives of each and every one of the camp's inhabitants; tragedies that stood out in stark relief when compared to the trials and hardships I'd experienced in my own life. Then I let the sadness be.

It suddenly struck me that, to a greater or lesser extent, sadness colours the background to all our lives. We are the same, united in our humanity by the fact that none of us can escape the experience of loss; in whichever of its myriad forms it may come. And because each moment is dependant on the loss of the moment before, it suddenly seemed vital that I appreciate the moment I was in, and be ready to embrace whatever the next might bring.

Sambana had picked up my bag, sandals and the AK and was carrying them to her hut. She put the sandals by the hut's entrance before opening its crude door of sticks and hemp-string, and placing the bag and AK inside.

'This is the place for your things, next to your sleeping place.' She closed the door again. 'Okay?'

'Fine by me,' I thought but said nothing.

Instead, I looked up into her brown-so-dark-they-looked-black eyes and embraced the moment. She held my gaze and sat down close by me.

The last segment of orange sky was glowing through the branches of the trees on the river's other bank. The basking crocodiles had been replaced by a family of hippos, taking their evening bath in the smooth waters as they gently flowed toward their mother, the River Nile.

'Let's eat!' Sambana said.

After having eaten our fill, we sat wrapped in a large cowhide Sambana had brought from her hut. With our backs resting against the log we stared into the fire's depths, as if trying to see our futures in the soft flames as they bathed our faces in their flickering glow.

Sambana pulled the cowhide tighter around our shoulders, pulling me closer to her. She rested her face on my chest, and my arm wrapped itself around her.

'I'm so happy you came here,' she whispered, 'because we'd never have met anywhere else. You've got a good heart, I can feel that, and you care about things in life that matter – like people, and what's right and wrong.'

Slowly letting go of Sambana I got up. I gave her my hand to help her rise and led her to the door of the hut. I kissed the tip of her nose before stepping into the hut's dark interior.

The soft glow of the Milky Way filtered through the open door, so many stars celebrating that moment in their procession across the heavens. I sat on the edge of her low, rustic wooden bed and let my eyes adjust to the light.

Nailed to the hut's wall, a rosary and small crucifix hung above the bed. I said a quiet prayer of thanks to the Almighty. Sambana stood soft like the night and fragile like the starlight. She dropped the cowhide onto the bed and reached behind her neck to loosen the tie that held her khanga in place. It fell to the floor in a fluid motion.

A warm, lambent radiance played over the contours of Sambana's naked body, as I reached out and drew her toward me.

TWELVE

It was already late in the morning, as we jogged single file into a small meadow in the middle of the bush. I'd left the camp the previous afternoon as part of a group of eighteen men. It was perhaps twelve days or so after Sambana had invited me to dinner, though it's hard to remember exactly as, for the days and nights following that magical evening, I was totally entranced.

The morning after our first night together, Sambana told me to bring my few things and move in with her. She said that it was her wish that her hut should be *our* home.

Sambana was the first person I ever felt I was really able to share myself with. I told her about my childhood, my family and my early adventures in Sweden's wilderness. With her, I was able to open up about the shame and humiliation I'd felt being mercilessly bullied and how it affected me; contributing to my sense of always being an outsider.

I told her how it had felt coming to Kenya and finding a group of people with whom I sensed some kind of affinity, then of finding her and feeling as if at last I'd found someone with whom I belonged.

'You belong with us,' she'd assured me. 'You believe in the things we believe in – that ordinary people, that people in

142

power don't seem to care about, should be able to live their lives free from fear and with dignity.'

I described the landscapes of my snow-swept homeland in the far north and told her the tales I remembered my mother telling me of our Viking ancestors. Sambana had learned a bit about Scandinavian history in school but her knowledge was coloured with the idea of the Vikings as barbarians. She soon realized this wasn't the case.

Of course it was not the same, but it struck me at the time, as being a bit like the misconceptions, fantasies, and stereotypes people have of Africa and its diverse people; misguided ideas and notions promoted to serve the interests of those who use ignorance to obscure truth.

When I told her about my ancestors she said she'd think of me as her warrior. 'You're my Viking in Africa, fighting for the cause of the just and oppressed.'

Sambana was the eldest of five siblings in a middle-class family. Both her parents had been educated and her father had been quite forward-thinking in relation to gender roles. He hadn't subscribed to the idea of women being subservient to men and had high expectations of his daughter. Though her education had been cut short, she had every intention of resuming it once the war was over.

I told her I could understand people thinking me crazy for giving up university but it had been something I had to do. I'd felt compelled, maybe by what a boy once called '*världsalltet*' – the 'world as a whole' or the 'universe'. I told her I call it 'The Great Flow'. She thought I was crazy for giving up my studies, but she also knew there was a guiding force behind our lives.

'I call it God,' she said, 'but it's the same thing. It's what's brought us together.'

Sambana shared some of the things I told her about myself with Jonathan. Maybe it helped him make a little sense of the mad boy who he'd found, barely alive in that village after the massacre. He certainly seemed a lot more relaxed around me and even ready to give me a chance. I think he could see that Sambana really felt something for me and I know that her happiness and wellbeing were paramount for him.

The day before we set off in the eighteen-man unit, he told me he was leading a group on a long-range mission to ambush four army trucks carrying medical supplies and rations, and powdered milk and machetes that the government distributed to the people in their attempt to bribe them. He asked if I wanted to volunteer but had warned me that it would be a long, hard slog and that we'd be jogging for much of the way to get to the place where they planned to ambush the convoy. He made it clear there was no room for passengers.

Jonathan was giving me a chance, albeit by dropping me in at the deep end. Without a second thought I told him I was 'in'. My involvement in the struggle was no longer just about an ideal; I was now there for Sambana, too.

We set off from the camp jogging in two groups, coming back together and walking through the night as one unit. While we moved steadily through the bush, Pole acted as the bloodhound for both groups: moving way ahead and returning from time to time to report back to Jonathan.

I've got no idea how far ahead of us Pole scouted but was sure he must have covered at least twice the distance we did. Other members of the unit carried his AKM, ammunition straps and small rucksack. All he carried with him was his assegai and bayonet-saw.

By the time we reached the meadow, on the morning after we'd set off, I was tired and also amazed at the stamina of the other men. It was their lead and example that helped me keep up with them and kept me going. Maintaining a steady breathing pattern, while keeping in rhythm with the man in front of me, I imagined we were carriages on a wagon train as we jogged.

My grandfather had worked on the railways in Sweden. I imagined him with me, riding an old train, looking down at the track running through forest and bush listening to the rhythmic breathing coming from the line of men that, to me, was like the rhythm of a steam train.

On reaching the meadow, the unit split in two again: one group followed Pole and the other Jonathan. I trotted fourth in line behind Jonathan.

By midday I was drenched in sweat and wondering how much further we had to go. Jonathan had warned me it would be hard and he was right. When he finally raised a hand signalling for us to stop, I let out a slow breath of relief. My inclination was to fall flat on the ground but I followed the men in front who quickly dropped to one knee. Jonathan and the two men behind him began cutting tufts of the yellow grass surrounding us and sticking them in handfuls into the folds of their clothing and equipment.

Before we'd left the camp Jonathan had taken me to one side. 'Pay attention and copy,' he'd told me. 'Look, think and learn!'

So I followed suit. The grass was sun-dried and brittle, not like the vegetation around the camp, or that I'd seen when at the village. The air was hot and heavy, throwing a torpid pall over the immediate landscape.

Crouched down as low as we could, we began moving forward and I figured that we'd almost reached our destination. All I could hear was the light swishing of grass and the occasional buzz of insects; there was no birdsong. The dry, still silence around us accentuated my fatigue but I had a feeling that getting there had been the easy part of the mission.

Signalling for me to remain a couple of metres to his side, Jonathan indicated for the others in our group to fan out. We'd reached the crest of a small hill overlooking a dirt road that ran upward from a shallow valley.

He told me to rest; drink some water, gnaw a bit off the salt rock he'd told me to bring and eat some of the dried fruit and nuts Sambana had given me.

'Then we'll swap,' he said. 'I'll rest and you watch the road.'

He outlined the guerrillas' plan of action for the ambush. As I tried to relax my aching muscles, I watched him scanning westward, in the direction the vehicles would be coming from. Our vantage point gave us a 100-metre clear view of the road as it appeared round a curve in the valley's side, ran upward along an incline before levelling out and continuing in a straight path between the hill we were on and a similar rise on the opposite side of the road; where Pole was hidden with his group.

I lay on my back and looked up at the cotton-wool clouds floating in the clear blue sky. I thought about the friends I'd left behind in Sweden who, at this very moment, were probably studying, playing tennis, hanging out together or taking their girlfriends out for a drive in their newly acquired cars. I felt the way I always had; that their world had never been mine. Whatever the reasons, my life had overstepped the boundaries that defined theirs.

Jonathan tapped me on the shoulder, pulling me back into the present. He looked at me intently. 'I want you to understand that I take no pleasure in killing my fellow countrymen, few of us do,' he said. Pointing at the Liverpool FC AK and Remington by my side, he continued. 'You've got your guns and I brought you here to use them. Something very ugly is about to take place here and it will all happen very fast. Despite the ugliness, pay attention and try to foresee things before they happen. Don't let what you see get to you or you will freeze. You need to remain detached and at the same time in total control of yourself.'

A lone bird of prey circled the sky in the distance over the valley. I watched it hover then dive out of sight behind the hill that obscured the road the trucks were approaching on. Did I feel scared? I don't think I did. Jonathan's words had brought the reality of the situation, and the task in hand, into sharp focus. We had gone there with a clear aim and, as Jonathan had said, it wasn't to kill people but to seize the goods in the backs of the trucks.

As he took his turn to rest, I peered through the grass at the dirt road, looking out for telltale signs of dust in the distance. Jonathan had told me that Heile, Moto and Baridi were lower down the slope, closer to the road and to the curve in the road that the trucks would be coming around.

I caught a glimpse of Heile arching his back in a cat stretch at one point while we were waiting, but the boys remained invisible; they were too well concealed. The boys seemed so young to be so close to the road and our targets. I wondered if because of their relatively small size they'd be less likely to be seen and, being so close, have a better chance of hitting the targets when the time came. The success of the mission being paramount, I guessed it was a case of the most fitting person for each role. In this sense everyone was equal – men and boys.

The afternoon was wearing on and I was beginning to wonder if the trucks would show up before sundown when Jonathan grabbed my shoulder and pointed. I followed the direction he was indicating and, sure enough, could make out a plume of dust rising in the distance. It was then the hammering sun and the itching grass gave way to a gnawing fear

I realized this was the first time ever I'd actually been the aggressor, seeking the fight rather than dealing with it when it came to me. It had always been a fundamental principle that I now seemed to be going against. 'Think of what Jonathan said... think of what Jonathan said...' repeated itself over and over in my head while I began to be able to hear the faint sound of diesel engines in the distance.

My breathing began to accelerate and a sense of panic rose in my chest. I took a lung-full of air and held it. The engine sound became clearer and I could now clearly distinguish more than one truck.

As I slowly exhaled the first lorry appeared around the corner of the hill, labouring up the steep incline toward us. As it approached, it threw up a cloud of dust immediately shrouding the second lorry no more than ten metres behind. Ten metres behind that, a third lorry appeared.

Without being aware of having picked it up, I found my Remington in my hands. I quickly checked to make sure it was loaded and placed the leading truck in its sights.

THIRTEEN

Jonathan had given the order that nobody was to start shooting until all four trucks had appeared around the corner and were within clear range. The first truck was now only 60 metres from us and there was no sign of the fourth.

I took a quick look in Jonathan's direction. His head was sticking just above the top of the grass and I realized the situation must be serious if he was risking exposing himself like that. I could hear him murmuring 'come on, come on, come on,' as the whine of the trucks' straining engines got closer and closer.

I scanned the opposite slope for signs of life but it was completely still, exactly the way it was supposed to be. It was a long, tough hill for the trucks to climb and the perfect place for an ambush, but where was the fourth lorry?

The first was now close enough for me to see two men inside its cab. I looked back down the road through the dust. Finally, coming around the corner from behind the hill I saw the fourth lorry struggling up the slope toward us.

A sharp report from Heile's gun below cut through the noise of the lorries' engines, catapulting the lead truck's driver's head and body backward in his seat. A split second later a hail of bullets crashed through the second lorry's windscreen, in one go taking out its driver and passenger.

At the same time, as the first and second lorries had been hit, the cabins of the third and fourth trucks were ravaged with bullets from the guns of the two boys in the grass by the roadside.

Watching the scene unfold through the grass was like covering my eyes and peering through my fingers. I wondered why these men had to be savagely killed, rather than held up and road-jacked at gunpoint. At one moment I saw men talking and laughing, only to see them slaughtered behind spiderwebs of shattered glass the next.

As the first truck was careering off the road toward Heile, the driver's mate desperately tried to push the dead man off him and gain control of the steering wheel. Springing out of the grass, Heile fired off a burst from his gun at the cab before running up the slope with the lorry up his backside.

As soon as the first shot had been fired I'd heard startled voices and shouting and wasn't sure where they were coming from but, as the lorry chased Heile up the hill, I realized there were men under the canvas of the first lorry's rear.

The voices became cries of alarm, panic and pain as the truck ran up the slope, tipped on its side and slid to a stop at the base of the hill.

The firing stopped abruptly after Heile's last rounds had left his gun. Running up the hill toward Jonathan and me he stopped and turned as if expecting to see the boys following him. For a second he seemed to consider going back to get them, but Jonathan was already pulling him down to take up position with us on the brow of the hill.

It became clear that the cries of alarm and confusion weren't just coming from the rear of the first lorry. The second truck had hit the opposite slope and stalled, the third had stopped abruptly in the middle of the road directly in front of Moto and Baridi, while the fourth had crashed into its back.

For a moment, a Babel of shouting cut through the billows of dust that seemed to be hanging over the road in the suddenly still air and then, from the backs of the four trucks, soldiers began spilling onto the ground. In that moment it was as if death itself took a momentary breath before blowing its hellfire onto the men below. Most of them fired their AKs wildly the second they hit the ground; both hillsides responded with a raging crossfire.

Hundreds of rounds rained down, cutting into and shredding the soldiers. The sound of automatic and semi-automatic firing was constant and so intense it was impossible to distinguish one shot from another. A cacophony of sudden pain and death turned the road below into a scene of carnage.

On the opposite hillside I could see the grass moving, as if being tickled by a gentle but lethal breeze, in front of barrels spitting down at the men below. Not a single shot was being fired into the canvas covering each truck's rear. The guerrillas knew their mission's goal was under that canvas, and with controlled discipline they avoided ruining the goods they'd come for.

Realizing I hadn't moved an inch, and maybe not even drawn a breath since the holocaust had begun, I filled my lungs and peered along the Remington's twin barrels, trying to get a handle on the scene unravelling below me. Spread out atop, and on each of the hillsides the guerrillas seemed to know exactly who was taking care of what, so I held back from joining in with the bloodbath.

I could see men desperately trying to take cover or escape the inferno by running away.

Some of the soldiers threw themselves under the lorries; others tried to hide behind their dead comrades. The next second I'd see puffs of smoke sprouting from their army-issue clothing which immediately turned a darker shade, or in a spattering of blood I'd see fabric being torn along with flesh and bone.

There was nowhere to run and nowhere to hide.

Scanning the scene down the barrel of my gun, my sights fell on a trio of bodies lying in a bloody mess by the third lorry about 40 metres from my position. Something about the bodies held my attention and then it clicked. The body in the middle of the trio was slowly twisting itself around and bringing its AK up over the body between it and the hill we were on.

It took me a few seconds to believe the soldier was actually alive, then I figured he'd escaped the rain of death by throwing himself between two of his fallen comrades and was now preparing to strike back. At the same time, I realized the man was directly opposite the boys' position at the base of the hill.

I shifted my position to get a better aim while he steadied his gun on the ribcage of the body that was covering him from the boys: I had to hurry. I wondered if the boys had seen him. I had the soldier fixed in the Remington's sights when my trigger finger froze. It felt as if I was about to commit a cold and calculated murder; so very far from what I'd felt in relation to my survival and self-defence when I'd killed the soldier at the roadblock. The body the man was resting his rifle on began moving beneath it. I realized the fallen soldier he was hiding behind was also alive, though badly wounded.

I was hit by a wave of compassion as the thought that this man needed help and care passed through my mind, meanwhile the soldier behind him was trying to hold his chest down in order to get a steady aim toward his target.

I tried to fight the conflicting thoughts raging through my mind, as the chest of the soldier the gun was resting on began to heave and its owner began coughing up thick clots of dark blood. I was doing exactly what Jonathan had warned me not to do; allowing my humanity and sanity to permeate the horror taking place in front of my eyes. I remembered what I'd learned at the roadblock: don't ask why, when or how – just do.

My grip tightened on the rifle and my trigger finger started to squeeze when the Remington was suddenly and violently torn from my hands.

'Fire your rifle. FIRE, damn it!' Jonathan screamed in rage. He fired both barrels in quick succession into the mayhem below before throwing the rifle back at me. He grabbed the Liverpool FC AK from the ground beside me and began firing that. Even more shocked and bewildered than before, I hurriedly reloaded the Remington before sweeping my sights through the parched yellow grass to find my target again.

As my sights swept past the second lorry, stalled against the opposite hillside, they caught the shadow of a soldier kneeling on one knee in the classic firing position, partly concealed by the truck's double tyres and pointing his AK directly toward our position.

'No one's seen him,' Little Man screamed.

The soldier between the bodies facing the boys went clean out of my head as bullets from the soldier beneath the second lorry began tearing up the ground in front of us. Earth flew up in Jonathan's face and he recoiled backward, shouting in pain and clutching his ear. In an instant I had the tyres and soldier's shadow in clear focus. As bullets from his rifle cut through the air around me the concern I'd felt about becoming a murderer disappeared. I pulled back the Remington's trigger and felt a dull, hard punch from its recoil in my shoulder. At the same time, there was an immediate double explosion from the tyres as the slug from my gun tore through them before slamming into the kneeling soldier with such force he was blown out from under the lorry's chassis.

Remembering the boys, I swung my rifle back to the ghoulish sandwich of bodies. The man in the middle was still, his AK awry across the body in front of him. I convinced myself the boys had seen him but all was quiet from the base of the hill.

An eerie stillness descended on the whole scene. To my side, Heile's voice punctured the silence. He was with Jonathan. Jonathan!

I remembered seeing him fall back after the man under the truck had fired at us. Heile was rinsing out Jonathan's eyes with water from a canteen and talking in a raised voice while Jonathan clutched his right ear. I guessed he'd taken an eyeful of flying earth and suffered a burst eardrum from a bullet hurtling a hair's breadth away from the side of his head, but he was still alive.

I lay on my back. Cotton wool clouds still hung in the sky above me, but I was now looking at them through a haze of grey smoke. I wondered how long it had been since I'd last watched them float in the sky. It felt like a lifetime. A lifetime in which I'd come to understand what Jonathan had meant when he'd described his world as 'grey'.

The people I'd identified as the 'good guys' had been the perpetrators of horrors I'd always associated with the 'bad guys'. Black and white had become eclipsed as the slaughter had unfolded. I'd seen it happen before: at the roadblock with Pole, in my willing the death of the baby instead of my own under the pile of bodies in the village.

I felt sickness and confusion envelop me, as the coherence and order of principles I'd clung to fractured and toppled into the dark maw of the human shadow.

At the time, I didn't have the vocabulary to interpret and analyze how I felt, but the feelings that overwhelmed me came from a realization that the absolute terms through which I'd filtered the world around me were completely adrift: good, evil; black, white; life, death; love, hate.

The points of reference that I'd always used to construct the appearance of a fixed and stable reality had slipped their moorings.

FOURTEEN

There can be no 'sweet' victory in war. We had secured our objective, but at what price?

I remember feeling as if we'd behaved just like the enemy. I felt as if I'd unwittingly allowed myself to be led on to the path of the wicked – the very path I'd gone there to oppose. At the same time I couldn't identify Jonathan or anyone else in his unit as 'wicked'. As Jonathan had emphasized, none of them took any pleasure in killing their fellow countrymen.

For my own part, throughout it all, I too didn't take any pleasure from killing, nor did I ever lose the feeling that it was fundamentally wrong. Like my mother, my grandfather had been a committed pacifist. Though completely opposed to their occupation of Sweden, he'd felt unable to play a part in the armed resistance to the German army during World War II. Instead, he became involved in peaceful acts of civil disobedience and disruption. My grandfather often came to my mind while I was in Uganda.

He never said you don't have the right to knock someone out of his socks if you had to but he didn't believe anyone had the right to take someone else's life. He'd also encouraged me never to be the one to start a fight. He was a man of peace and love and I'd always liked his philosophy, but in Uganda I was on a train that was already rolling and couldn't be stopped. Little Man and I often argued about this until he gradually became silent. I guess I couldn't deal with the internal conflict.

I soon discovered that Baridi had been killed and most probably, I thought, by the soldier I'd seen on the ground in front of the boys' position. During the aftermath, as the rebels divided and stowed the valuable supplies and equipment in the three remaining trucks, Moto ruthlessly executed the few survivors.

His act of revenge sent Jonathan into a rage and Heile had to restrain him from physically beating the boy. There was no sweet sense of achievement in our success and for me, far from it: if Baridi had been killed by the soldier I'd seen and failed to shoot, I was culpable.

I later discovered that the supplies in only one of the trucks were going back to our camp; rebels from other units who'd joined us to take part in the ambush were loading the other two. As well as taking supplies, equipment, arms, ammunition, uniforms and money found on bodies, the rebels stripped the toppled lorry of its wheels and engine parts. The operation was executed with as fierce an efficiency as the ambush.

Within a short space of time, and as dusk approached, we were ready to move out. But there was to be no free ride back for me. Whatever the rationale, it had been decided that I was to make my way back to the camp on foot with Moto. When Heile told me I threw up; finally succumbing to the nausea that had gripped me since the final stages of the ambush.

'Don't worry, you'll never get used to it,' Heile said. 'And as long as it's so, at least you know you're still alive.'

Thinking about the glazed-over and dead look I'd seen in the eyes of the soldier at the roadblock I figured Heile was right; it wasn't the kind of thing a human being should get used to.

It took Moto and me three days and nights to find our way back to the camp. For the whole of our trek I paid close attention to what he did and how he did it. Throughout the time I was in the bush with the rebels there were very few occasions in which I remember anyone ever using a map or compass. Even at his relatively young age, Moto had learned how to travel without the tools for orienteering, just as I had as a boy.

By using prominent landmarks on the ground, the sun, moon and stars, by registering the terrain, its particular species of shrubs and trees, and the wildlife, and by developing a keen sense of direction, it was possible to create a 'map' in the mind. How much he'd memorized on our way there and how much Jonathan, Pole or Heile had briefed him for the return trip I don't know, but he managed to get us home.

I never mentioned the soldier who might have killed Baridi and discovering that he and Moto were twins only added to my sense of guilt. Throughout our journey back Moto didn't talk much, but what he told me about himself and his brother seemed to fit an increasingly familiar pattern.

An armed group had attacked the village they'd lived in with their family. He and his brother had been spared death but forced to join the group. Sambana had told me that there were many different groups living in, and operating out of, the bush. Many of them, like Jonathan's unit, were well disciplined and loyal to the NRA and its aims, but others were little more than bandits that preyed on government troops and innocent villagers alike. It was one of these groups that Moto and Baridi had been forced to join.

Moto described how the group had eventually split, as individuals within it fought for control. The group that he and his brother had ended up with had tried to ambush a unit Jonathan was on patrol with, only to end up being surrounded by Jonathan and his men.

In the firefight that ensued most of the group was killed but before their total annihilation Jonathan had offered its remaining members amnesty as guerrilla fighters in his group, or their freedom to run away if they gave up their weapons.

Moto and Baridi were the first to come to a decision; approaching Jonathan as the two groups held their fire and, with their AKs over their heads in one hand and the magazines to their guns in the other, they'd asked to fight with his group. Though, at first, he'd been reluctant to adopt child soldiers into his unit – he'd thought they'd have a greater chance of survival with him.

As we made our way through the bush back to the camp, I thought about Moto's life in relation to my own. I estimated that when he and Baridi had been forced to join the group that had attacked their village, he would have been about the same age that I'd been when I was getting beaten by the young thugs in the town we'd moved to; a time when the knowledge of an unjust world was being etched into me.

This formative experience was very much a part of why I'd wanted to join the rebels and gave me a deep sense of empathy with these people who'd been cast as the underdog.

Moto had cried when he'd told me his story during the second night of our hike back. We'd climbed a tree in which we planned to sleep, having heard a pack of lions Moto had said sounded hungry prowling the bush.

I felt humbled by Moto's resilience. He'd just lost his twin brother, maybe the only surviving member of his immediate family but it just seemed to strengthen his resolve to continue the struggle 'to be free and make a better life', as I heard so many people say. He didn't seem to have any illusions, and suddenly illusions seemed like a luxury – a folly even.

I realized I'd come to Uganda with my own illusions and that, one by one, they were being shattered. Maybe that was an illusion, too, but I still felt strongly committed to being a part of a righteous struggle for freedom from oppression and tyranny. Even if that meant creating its own tyranny, like the bloodbath I'd just been a part of.

Hearing about the ways that different groups operated, and having an idea of what probably motivated them, I believed Jonathan's strategy was always a means to an end rather than an end in itself. He wasn't a bad man, nor were Pole or Heile. They were people dealing with a situation and attempting to exert a degree of control over circumstances that had got way out of control.

I didn't believe love was an illusion either. As we hiked back I thought about Sambana. At first I wondered if what had happened had merely been an overriding need for human contact or some kind of crush. Then I realized how much I missed her and wanted to be with her and how strangely at ease and at peace I felt when I was with her.

When we got back to the camp and I saw her again I realized how real my feelings were. The horror of the ambush and my feelings of culpability over Baridi's death faded then almost disappeared the moment I was back with Sambana in our home on the banks of the river under the flame tree.

I'm not sure if it was Jonathan's intention but by the time we got back to the camp I felt as if something inside me had changed. It was as if during the walk back I assimilated the experiences I'd had over the past months in Uganda. Though at the time I didn't think about it consciously, during that walk back it was as if I became my new persona; I became 'Lucky'.

When Jonathan welcomed me back I had a sense of his finally having accepted me, and felt he welcomed me as a fellow-in-arms. There was no mention of the ambush, of how I'd performed as a 'soldier' in the situation and of what I'd done, or failed to do. Even so, Baridi's death really got to me and I felt a burden of guilt. Maybe it helped that during the weeks that followed I finally began to feel integrated into life in the camp.

People got used to having this strange guy around and any earlier suspicions gave way to familiar and friendly smiles.

Of course, the fact that Sambana and I were living together helped people to accept me; as Jonathan's niece and the hospital's nurse Sambana was a highly respected member of the camp's community.

While Alex's village had been very close to the area of Uganda most affected by the civil war, Jonathan's camp was further north. Its community was made up of people who had chosen to take up arms and their families, and a number of people who were non-combatants but had been displaced by the conflict.

After what Sambana had said to me during our first evening together I came to think of it as a refugee camp of sorts; a very well-defended one. The hospital sometimes tended to the sick and wounded from elsewhere, and the fact that rebels from other units had taken part in the ambush made me realize we were part of an extended network.

People just tried to stay alive and get by, doing their bit to contribute to the struggle and awaiting the victory that everybody believed would come.

The government had begun to use helicopter gunships against the rebels and, though we were out of the main area of government-focused attention, our biggest threat was potentially from being spotted by a helicopter's crew. We were never flown over but the need for total concealment was ever-present. The fractured memories of the massacre in the village that came back to me included the image of rotor blades over a charred building.

A complex series of lookouts and regular and extended patrols secured the camp's perimeter and also helped protect local 'friendly' villages from government forces and bandits alike. The camp had two neighbouring fishing villages that supplied us with dried fish in return for protection and healthcare. Sambana and I lived off the fresh fish we caught with homemade rods, from a ledge cut out of the river's bank just below the platform.

People in the camp had little vegetable plots dotted around and so were able to be relatively self-sufficient though, as Sambana told me, nobody was eating as well as they used to and though nobody starved, hunger was sometimes an issue.

As well as impacting on Uganda's people, the civil war had also affected its wildlife. With a decimated rural infrastructure, and a significant number of government and rebel troops living in the field, there were whole areas that were over-hunted for bush meat.

On our journey back from the ambush, Moto had told me that was why the lions we'd heard were hungry and it was in situations like that, he'd said, that they'd happily turn to humans to fill their stomachs.

Being able to supplement a meagre diet with foodstuffs hijacked from a military convoy was important. Much of our share of the supplies and produce from the ambush was being stored at a friendly location 50 kilometres north of the camp, and being brought back when needed.

I kept a close eye on Moto after we got back. Though his resilience seemed self-evident, I wanted to make sure he was okay.

When I told Sambana that Baridi had been killed during the ambush she went very quiet, as if withdrawing to process the news, and then she came back. Because of the positivity, warmth and joy she exuded it was easy to forget that Sambana's life had been punctuated by so much tragedy and suffering.

As she withdrew and then returned, I wondered if she created individual compartments inside herself in which she laid to rest each piece of sad news.

Jonathan showed his concern for the boy, too. As soon as we were back he took Moto off weapons' maintenance and sent him to work for Mama Palma Vini. Visiting Moto at Mama Palma Vini's duka in the weeks after the ambush I could see Jonathan's reason. Several of the orphaned children living in the camp had adopted her as their surrogate mother and, as I got to know her, I could see why.

She'd been a schoolteacher before being driven from her home by the war and while she was strict, she was also very warm and caring. By putting Moto to work in her duka Jonathan knew that he would become integrated into Mama Palma Vini's 'family' and acquire a whole new set of step-siblings.

With Sambana, those weeks after the ambush were like a strange, unanticipated, wonderful, extended and totally blissful honeymoon. In the time and space we'd been given we talked, laughed and made love a lot. We were like kids in our own private universe. We fished from the ledge over the river, watching the fishermen from the local villages strenuously making their way upriver in pirogues, fighting against the current using long poles as punts and then returning downstream happy or miserable, depending on the size of their catch.

I helped out with odd jobs that needed doing in and around the hospital tent. We gave John a glorious send-off when he left the hospital and the camp, to live with family near the Kenyan border, where things were a bit calmer. He wanted all the credit for bringing Sambana and me together, and I happily gave it to him.

The magic I'd felt on the day that John had persuaded Sambana to give my feet some TLC hadn't gone away but, like an endless silken thread, seemed to extend as the days went by. What seemed incredible was that we both acknowledged the same depth of feeling, so that when we lay in each other's arms sharing our dreams for a future together it didn't seem odd or unreal but the most natural thing in the world. We'd been lonely souls but no longer. Now we were souls shining and one. Daring in all; believing in the outcome that, in our hearts, we longed for.

FIFTEEN

Sambana and I talked about the future a lot. I noticed it was generally what people in the camp tended to do. The people I knew didn't talk about the war unless some relief was needed, and they didn't talk about the past, but they certainly talked about their plans for the future, and the future always seemed bright somehow. They also seemed much more able to appreciate and value the present moment.

The first time I really noticed this was on the final evening of our 'honeymoon'.

Sambana and I were waiting for our dinner to finish grilling on the flat stone by the fire. The sun was going down behind the flame tree and the forest's shadows stretched themselves across the river below us. All of a sudden, and as if he'd dropped from the sky, Pole was there on the platform.

I'd always thought of the platform as being a pretty secure location, as it was bordered by the river's high, steep bank and impenetrable forest undergrowth, with the path being the only access. The fact that when we noticed him, Pole was on the adjacent side of the platform to the path meant he'd either fallen from the heavens or come through the bush, which was so dense it surely would have torn his skin. However he'd got there; it had been without a sound.

I was sure he wouldn't have moved from the spot he was standing, nor maybe even drawn a breath until we'd seen and greeted him. His sudden presence took me by surprise, while Sambana simply jumped up and greeted him in their unusual forehead, eyes and nose style. She invited him to eat with us, while taking his hand and leading him to a place next to us by the fireside. He quickly made it clear that though he was very happy to eat with us, he'd come for me rather than dinner.

I felt stunned. Soon after Moto and I had got back to camp Jonathan had told me to recuperate in preparation for a scouting mission he wanted me to go on with Pole. That had been a few weeks ago and I'd forgotten about it. I could hardly give the excuse that I couldn't go because I wasn't quite ready to bring my honeymoon to an end. Sambana, on the other hand, expressed nothing but joy at seeing Pole.

She knew that each and every minute counted and getting upset about something in the future was merely going to turn the present moment sour, even if that future was imminent. She may well also have been taken aback by the turn of events but she had the strength of character to rise above feelings that could have brought her down and instead appreciate the short time she still had with me. The thing is, she knew that the reality of the circumstances we were in were such that the time we had together could possibly be the last time we'd have together.

It was a sobering thought.

As we ate, I made a joke to Pole that his not taking the path to the platform had probably meant he'd trampled on the flowers I'd planted in the bush. He'd given me a curious look, as if believing I had actually planted flowers and surprised that he hadn't noticed them. He made a comment about not understanding why anyone would want flowers in such a dark place.

Several minutes passed, as we quietly savoured Sambana's tasty cooking, then suddenly, and without looking up from his dinner, he commented:

'But if you planti such a whiti seed in such a darki place, you will see such a beautiful thingi...!'

Sambana and I looked at each other, as what he was saying hit us. A huge smile spread across Sambana's face. She leapt up, tossing her still half-full bowl at me and began dancing round the platform, spinning around while hooting with joy at the darkening dusk sky. Watching her over the brim of his own bowl and without stopping eating, he turned to me with a full mouth and a warm, kind smile on his face.

'Crazy girl!' He said.

We left after dinner, as soon as I'd had a chance to gather together the things Pole told me to bring with me. I asked him how long he was planning on being in the bush.

'Two weeks... three maybe – we'll see,' was the indefinite answer I got. He continued: 'Bring Tor, it shoots good with you – man under lorry, BOOM!'

After the incident at the roadblock I'd said I thought the Remington was like Thor's hammer and then told him about the Old Norse God. He'd obviously remembered. What surprised me though was the fact that he'd been aware of me hitting the soldier behind the tyre. I wondered what he didn't see and asked him if he knew how Baridi had been hit. He told me he didn't.

We carried very little with us: our weapons and ammunition, two full canteens of water each, a blanket each in a hide cover, some bush meat and two bags of dried cashew nuts Sambana had given us. She'd produced two bags of freshly roasted cashews and tried to pack one in my bag, giving Pole a cheeky, mock-bemused look when he'd frowned at her. She'd retreated back into her hut and came out with two skin bags of dried nuts, which she dutifully opened and held under Pole's nose.

Sambana knew the strong aroma of the roasted nuts would have broadcast our presence to the least-skilled tracker and was teasing Pole, maybe to delay our departure, because when we finally said our farewells I could see she had to twist her face into the brave look she presented.

Food was the number-one priority in the bush. You'd never wait till you'd run out before thinking about 'shopping' for the next meal and if you came across it by chance you'd usually never miss the opportunity to grab what you could. Hunting for it, while on the move, was also not something you'd normally want to do. It could take you far off your track and also distract you from your mission.

Every action had to be balanced against your immediate needs, your situation and circumstances and your mission's aim. The food we carried with us was for emergencies; if we became cut-off or unable to find anything edible. When we were out in the bush we lived mainly off the land; grubs, snakes, birds and small mammals, roots and fruits. Salt was very important, too; I always carried a block of rock salt and, of course, water was essential.

We struck refreshingly lucky on our fifth day in the bush when we came across a couple of grand old mango trees. Both their giant crowns were laden with fruit and we spent a good half an hour eating as much as we could. Afterwards, we walked on; passing the ruin of an old house or farmstead that had once stood there. It had been built in red brick, which more than likely meant it had belonged to white people. I wondered if it had belonged to 'settlers'.

Uganda's rich and fertile land and lush vegetation, its abundance of fresh water and relatively cool climate, particularly in areas that reach up to 2,000 metres above sea level, had earned it Winston Churchill's accolade as 'The Pearl of Africa'. It had also singled the country out, along with neighbouring Kenya, for agricultural colonization.

Uganda's northern region though, where Pole and I were tracking, was generally hotter, with less lush, dense vegetation.

All that was left of that reminder of a previous époque was a metre-tall brick outline of a house and rooms and its pair of magnificent mango trees.

We'd come across the place while scouting a five-man government foot patrol. The soldiers had led us to the trees, eaten their fill and then left their tracks for us to follow after we'd done the same. We followed them for the rest of the day and into the evening until, two hours after nightfall, they decided to set up camp among a patch of trees and bushes, in a landscape dominated by tall grass.

Pole and I climbed a tree, about 100 metres from their camp, from where we watched them sitting around their modest fire. I always found it hardest to stay awake between 3:00 and 6:00 and at some point in the early hours my mind had switched off only to be brought back by Pole poking my foot with his assegai from the ground below.

The soldiers' fire was no longer glowing and, as I slipped out of the tree, I wondered if they'd already broken camp. As Pole set of into the tall grass I put a hand on his shoulder and pulled him down to a squat.

'What's going on?' I asked.

'Nothing,' was his terse reply.

He began to stand up but I continued to try to get some kind of explanation out of him.

'Are we still following the soldiers?'

He just shot me a glance from standing and sped like a leopard into the tall grass, with me hot on his heels. He seemed to be heading directly for the soldiers' camp. I was following a few metres behind with my rifle and preparing myself to be ready for anything. Within seconds we were in among the trees where the soldiers were camped and an instant later in their camp itself.

I know that the way I remember what happened next defies the laws of physics, so maybe couldn't have happened like that, but many of the things I witnessed Pole do defied the laws of physics so my memory might be correct. As we ran without stopping through their camp, continuing into the grass on the other side of the clump of trees, Pole used his assegai and bayonet-saw as if they were extensions of his body; unleashing a silent whirlwind of death on all but one of the soldiers.

In my mind's eye, I've got an image of a soldier sitting against a tree looking at us in utter shock as we tore through the camp. Another soldier on his back with a blanket over his shoulders, probably on guard duty and the first to go. The other three still, lifeless under their blankets.

It wasn't for me to judge, or even ask Pole why he'd done what he did. I knew he'd killed the enemy and I figured that sadly this was a big part of what war was all about. I'd no idea of the details of his past, apart from the few anecdotes I'd already heard, and I didn't know what motivated the way he operated.

In the aftermath of the ambush I watched him press his open palm over the mouth and nose of a wounded soldier, suffocating him to prevent him alerting soldiers that were still in the back of one of the trucks that he was stealthily creeping toward. When he'd cut out the tongues of the soldiers at the roadblock he hadn't been collecting trophies but making a point about the possible consequences of 'talking shit'.

I knew he wasn't pathologically cruel and wouldn't indulge in torture or inflict needless suffering, but I think he saw the lives of his enemies as his for the taking. I figured he'd left that soldier in the camp alive so that he'd be able to let his comrades know exactly whom they were up against in this conflict: sowing the seeds of fear and undermining morale.

War tends to be told from the top down, yet its cruel reality is most acutely felt from the ground up. Without doubt, war impacts on countries, economies and the macrocosmic course of world histories, yet its most profound impact is felt at the level of the individual and the particular, rather than in the general.

The large brushstrokes used to represent and report wars tend to serve to obscure its horrific details. The reality is the fear and suffering it inflicts on all living things that fall within its wake. I imagined a traumatized foot soldier telling his platoon commander how he'd watched his unit exterminated by a little man with a bayonet-saw and assegai.

Pole and I barely spoke during our time in the bush but the attention I gave to everything he did made up for the silence. It was often hard for me to understand his rationale but I knew he always had one so I watched carefully and absorbed what I could of his aeons' old wisdom. Since then I've drawn on elements of that wisdom time and again.

Though there were some things he showed me that I'll never forget, some of them I'll never be able to imitate or explain. One of these took place during our last few days on that particular bush patrol.

SIXTEEN

I'd been following Pole as he tracked a trio of female lions through dry savannah and, though I didn't have much of a clue why he was following them, I dutifully tagged along as he stalked the big cats.

After a couple of hours on their tails, and having maintained what felt like a relatively safe distance from them, Pole pointed out a small group of adult and young zebra in the distance. The lionesses had noticed them too, fanning out in the long grass as they approached the herd.

On several occasions while we were following them I had the feeling that the lionesses knew we were there. A couple of times when they'd stopped, one or other of the trio seemed to look back in our direction. If they did know we were there they were obviously after another kind of prey and not interested in us.

I was sure Pole knew they'd sensed us too, but it didn't seem to concern him. He always made sure we were tracking them from positions that wouldn't allow the gentle breezes rustling through the grass to carry our scent their way. Since the lions already seemed to be aware of us, I figured this had to do with Pole not wanting to upset them with our presence and disturb their hunting.

We stopped at a distance of about 80 metres from the grazing zebras; crouching low but peering over the tall grass. Once we were no longer moving I began to feel quite vulnerable. I didn't want to become the alternative to zebra on the lionesses' menu, but had faith that Pole knew exactly what he was doing. As I watched, I noticed a line of grass in front of me being separated, as one of the cats moved in on its prey.

I glanced at Pole. He was looking intently in the direction of the zebras; fully alert, crouched low but with his body slightly bent forward and holding his assegai like a lance to one side. Totally in the moment, I felt a wave of anticipation and excitement pass through me.

Up ahead the zebras suddenly exploded from a standing-start to a full-on gallop. Pole and I simultaneously shot up to better see the chase.

Like ground-to-ground missiles, and approaching the fleeing herd on individual trajectories, three V-shaped lines snaked swiftly through the grass. Immediately before point of impact, one of the lionesses launched herself into the air; razor-sharp claws just missing the rump of one of the fleeing herd, as the zebra leapt up and kicked backward with its hooves in a terrified defence.

The failed attack gave the herd time to regroup, with the younger ones getting in and among the zebras' leaders. While the big cat that had missed its prey seemed to lose momentum, the others picked up their pace behind and to the right of the herd. The zebras began to weave left and right trying to outrun their pursuers.

At the same time, I noticed the grass snaking at an angle toward the herd's left flank. I guessed it must have been the lioness that'd missed her first target now coming back into the chase.

Pole was watching the hunt with a smile on his face as if he was at a Saturday afternoon sports event. I still had no idea why he was taking me through this experience, but I knew that if the lions lost their quarry we could be next.

Perhaps sensing the pincer movement of their hunters, the zebras did a tight full turn to the left and began galloping at full speed back toward Pole and me. For the first time in what felt like ages I heard Little Man in my head: 'Shit!'

It was clear the zebras were trying to wear the lionesses down in order to be able to make their escape, but they were doing it in our direction.

The two lionesses on the herd's right followed the zebras, swinging around to their left, but now the third lioness, which had been heading towards the zebras' left, was fast closing in on the centre of their right side. A few of the herd sensed the imminent danger and wildly turned in their tracks away from the oncoming threat.

Almost as one the rest followed, but like a guided missile the lioness was zeroing in at such a speed that escape for all was impossible. One of the younger zebras was hit with such force both it and its assailant flew out of view into the long grass. Within seconds the other two had joined in the kill.

The herd stopped running at a safe distance from the lionesses and looked back in the direction of their fallen fellow. I wondered what they were feeling. I had no doubt that they felt something. Observing the behaviour of wildlife, as we trekked through the bush, had reinforced this notion I had that we're not so different from other animals: just more complex, maybe.

Pole pulled me by my sleeve so I was standing closer to him. 'I do job fast,' he said, fixing my eyes with his. 'Stay by me and watch the lions but don't shoot, okay?' I had the feeling I was about to find out why we'd been following the beasts.

Keeping hold of my sleeve he led me into the grass. With eyes above the top of the grass, crouching low and moving at a pace, I followed Pole toward the spot where the lioness had taken down the zebra. My attention was focused 100 per cent on what he was doing because I knew my life was totally in his hands.

When he slowed down and crouched even lower I followed suit. Within seconds, through the tall grass, I saw the three lionesses feasting on their prey.

Without stopping, Pole raised himself to his full height and stepped into the clearing in the grass, created when the zebra had been taken down.

They were so busy feeding that at first they didn't seem to be aware of us, and then I noticed their ears suddenly laying down flat on their heads. Pole continued his steady approach but at an even slower pace. I stayed close behind, as he'd instructed me.

As we made our approach, I felt Pole's total presence in the moment. I also felt a sense of supreme confidence and purpose emanating from him. It totally eradicated any apprehension I was feeling.

In the midst of the lions, the sense of intention he projected was completely free of any hint of threat; there was nothing about Pole's body language that suggested he intended to attack the lionesses, or that he feared them.

The zebra's carcass was on its side, with its innards bared to the elements and, while the lionesses gorged themselves on its organs they kept their eyes firmly fixed on us. Intent on securing one of its rear legs, Pole moved toward the zebra's hindquarters where one of the lionesses was feeding on its sex organs.

Our approach meant the lioness had to change positions in order to keep a good eye on us. Without letting go of her meal she climbed over the rigid leg, twisting the carcass so the leg jutted up into the air between her and us.

Calmly, and without any sign of aggression toward the feeding lions, he levelled his assegai to the height of his head and with a quick, powerful and precise downward movement sliced its blade through the zebra's hip. The three lionesses twitched and a low gurgle rumbled in their throats.

Pole remained still, his assegai buried in the zebra's flesh as if he was telling them that he was now disarmed and at their mercy, if they wanted to do anything about the situation. I prepared myself for a change in their mood but kept my rifle slightly down, rather than pointed directly at the big cats.

With the situation back under control Pole began casually cutting through the rest of the zebra's leg, his blade moving back and forth inches away from the nearest female's fangs. She was chewing into the flesh next to the nice meaty piece of hip Pole intended for us.

Once through flesh and bone, he pulled the severed leg toward himself with the long, razor-sharp blade of his assegai in one motion.

Though their ears remained down and their eyes never left us, they hadn't stopped feeding and seemed to accept giving up a bit of their catch, rather than interrupting their meal and getting into a fight with a couple of non-threatening humans.

With the zebra's leg over his shoulder, Pole reversed for a couple of metres before turning his back and walking along the same path we'd taken to get there. I wasn't quite as brave or confident and couldn't help myself from keeping my eyes over my shoulder; looking back at the scene I'd just witnessed and survived.

When he'd first seen the lions, Pole had known they were prowling for a meal. He also knew that if they got lucky we'd be able to share in their good fortune and not have to look for any more food during the rest of our time in the bush.

Pole found us a place to stop and treat the meat. After he'd skinned the leg we cut it into long, thin slices, which we laid out to dry in the sun. I wondered why Pole hadn't just fired his AK to scare the lions away once they'd killed the zebra. I figured it just wasn't his way, after all the lions weren't his enemy and it would have been totally disrespectful to steal the fruits of their labour. He was also very careful never to draw unnecessary attention and there was no knowing who else might have heard the gunshots.

Whatever his reasons, Pole definitely had a style all of his own – he was truly one of a kind.

SEVENTEEN

As Pole and I were heading back to the camp after our time in the bush, all I could think about was seeing Sambana again. It felt like we'd been away for months, maybe because the whole experience had been such an incredible learning curve. I had the feeling Jonathan knew it would be, and that was why he'd sent me.

When I got back to our home by the river Sambana was nowhere to be seen. The cooking fire under the flame tree was smouldering and nearly out, and she wasn't on the fishing ledge, so I guessed she was probably at the hospital.

It was getting toward late afternoon, one of my favourite times of the day. The sun's intensity was beginning to ease, revealing the beauty of nature's multiple colours and textures, as the day's glaring light started to soften.

Standing on the river bank, I used Sambana's bucket-on-a-rope to haul up a few buckets of water from the river and scrubbed myself clean. I was ready for my princess. It felt really good to be home again. As I was drying myself by the log I didn't notice Sambana coming toward me on the path until I felt a sharp, stinging smack.

I spun round and she leapt into my arms. 'There I've branded you! Now you'll never be able to escape,' she said, bubbling over with laughter as I craned my head around to see the red print of her hand on my white-as-snow backside.

She covered my face in kisses as I spun her around the platform, until I lost my balance and we crashed to the ground with her on top of me. A look of concern passed over her face.

'Are you okay?' I asked, worried that I'd hurt her.

'I've got to be careful,' she said, suddenly looking rather serious. With her face over mine, and as my blue eyes stared into her brown-so-dark-they-looked-black eyes, she continued: 'I don't want anything to happen to our baby.'

My heart skipped a beat. 'Come again,' I blurted out, caught by surprise. I wasn't sure I'd heard her right.

'I'm going to have your baby, Lucky.' She replied, with an edge of anxiety in her voice, as if suddenly unsure how I was going to respond to the news.

Then it was my turn to cover her face in kisses and our kisses were dissolved by the tears both of us cried; tears of joy, tears of relief, tears of gratitude for the gift of each other and for the gift of our love – a new life.

'I want to have your baby, Lucky,' Sambana said through her smiles and tears, 'because I know you know how to love, and because you have a heart that feels.'

Pole had been right. In retrospect, I can see he was just using common sense and knew that there was a good chance that Sambana might get pregnant, but at the time it seemed as if he'd peered into a crystal ball. Despite the circumstances, or maybe even *because* of the circumstances, it just felt *so* right.

It was as if the path that had taken me into Nairobi's slum, to Moses and then to Uganda, had all the while been leading to this. At the time, and in that moment, it felt as if neither Sambana nor I had any control over the matter of bringing a child into the world. It felt like we were caught up in a situation that was so much bigger than us and that all we really had to hold on to was our love.

I wasn't sure then at what level we have free will, and I'm still not really sure. I know I'd chosen to go to the slum in Nairobi, but it was as if the bar in which I'd met Moses and his friends had found me. I know I made the decision to drop out of university in Sweden and return to Nairobi and join a rebel group in Uganda, but Jonathan found me and neither Sambana nor I had been looking for each other.

The way I felt when Sambana told me she was pregnant was that if it was to be, then it was to be and the reason for its being belonged entirely to världsalltet – The Great Flow.

I'd wanted to join a righteous cause in its stand against tyranny and when I'd found Sambana my stand became personal and not just about principles and ideology; even more so now she was pregnant. Suddenly, the dreams we'd shared for our future seemed like they were starting to materialize, and my stake in the struggle was no longer just about Sambana but about our family. As we lay in each other's arms later that night, listening to the resonant chirruping of thousands of crickets through the hut's open door, I felt the strange sense of dislocation I'd felt before.

'It's hard to believe there's a war being fought out there,' I said, feeling the peace of a slumbering land creeping in from the world outside.

'That's how it is,' Sambana replied, her head resting on my chest. 'One moment we're in our boat on life's river – laughing... fishing... happy. Then suddenly, a rock appears where there was no rock before and crash! The boat is sunk. And while we were laughing, on the river bank the hungry crocodiles were waiting.'

The reality of our situation came back to me. 'Let me take you to Nairobi. You could stay with my parents till the war's over,' I said.

'While you return here and risk your life on that boat with the rocks and crocodiles?' She replied. 'I'm not running from my country and I'm needed in the hospital. It's not much but it's my part in all the madness. Anyway, your parents think you're in Sweden; then I show up with my big belly?'

I laughed, but felt uneasy. Madness is unpredictable at best and raging at worst.

'It will end soon, Lucky. You'll see. They can't carry on fighting us forever, we're too strong for them and we're too many.'

Sambana was talking about the government and she was right, the war wasn't going their way.

Although I had no idea at the time, I'd actually entered Uganda as the tide was turning in favour of the NRA. The Ugandan army was literally falling apart. Throughout the civil war recruits to the army often received very little training, were poorly equipped, not fed properly or paid regularly. As the war progressed their conditions deteriorated. Coupled with a general lack of discipline, groups of soldiers had formed themselves into gangs of bandits that were terrorizing the civilian population.

This served to increase popular support for the NRA and also made it easier for them to dominate the conflict militarily. It also led to an increase in atrocities against civilians and an increasingly anarchic situation in particular areas on the ground.

When Sambana told Jonathan she was pregnant, like me he wanted her to leave the country. He actually admitted that he'd been happy for our relationship to develop for that very reason, hoping that I'd take her back to Sweden. Jonathan tried to talk her into leaving but she was adamant that she wanted to stay.

The government seemed to be on the verge of collapse and, while Jonathan and I thought it would be by far safer for her

179

to have our baby out of the country; her response was that the war could be over by the time she gave birth. I felt torn. The situation was incredibly volatile and, while we were outside the main areas of conflict and as well hidden within the bush as we could be, there was no guarantee that the war wouldn't somehow find us.

Short of taking her out of the country against her will she wasn't going to change her mind, so Jonathan came up with another solution.

Our share of the supplies we'd seized during the ambush was being stored at a mission station, whose head priest was sympathetic to the rebels and their cause. Father Giuseppe ran the mission. He was an Italian priest who'd been in Uganda for many years and whom both Jonathan and Sambana knew well.

A small community had grown up around the station and, as well as its spiritual work, the mission also provided basic health care. Amenities at the station were far better than they were in the camp and Jonathan thought it would be a better place for Sambana to have our baby. He also thought it was relatively safe. While churches and missions weren't immune from attack, their being targeted was rare.

It was a compromise Sambana agreed to; she'd be able to continue the work she felt committed to but have access to fresh running water and a more varied diet. Infant mortality was an issue in Uganda and made worse by the war. We all wanted our baby to have the best chance for survival. It was also close enough to the camp for me to make regular visits to Sambana while remaining active with Jonathan's unit.

Sambana wanted to remain in the camp for as long as possible, but by the time she was halfway through the pregnancy Jonathan and I were able to persuade her to relocate.

For some reason Jonathan called Giuseppe's mission 'The Heart'; I never did ask why, but it might have had something to do with Father Giuseppe himself; he was certainly a man with a big heart. He'd come to Uganda soon after World War II, when he was in his thirties, and had never left.

One of 12 brothers and sisters, he'd come from a poor family in Southern Italy. He told me that as a boy he'd had two options for his future – policeman or priest. His parents had pushed him toward joining the priesthood and he'd entered a seminary as a young man. He told me that he would have preferred to become a policeman but didn't feel able to challenge his parents' wishes.

Soon after finishing seminary he'd asked to become a missionary. He said he'd felt at odds with the extent to which the Catholic Church dominated people's lives in Italy. While he held a firm belief in God, and felt that a moral and spiritual dimension should play a part in our lives, he believed it should be something that people came to freely, rather than through fear and control.

From what I saw, it was obvious that he was incredibly successful in his work, and I'm sure it had a lot to do with his approach. He never tried to force his faith on anyone, nor suggested that people were wrong to follow other beliefs and traditions, and was comfortable with people incorporating them into Catholic beliefs and practices.

Despite the expulsion of Italian Catholic missionaries during the 1970s, he'd managed to survive the excesses of Amin's years in power. Like many, he'd hoped for better from Obote but had very soon become disillusioned. Museveni's stated intention to create a new Uganda, united across ethnic lines, resonated with the old priest and he was committed to supporting the NRA's cause.

Giuseppe had adopted Uganda as his home and it was clear that his 'flock' had wholeheartedly adopted him. He told me Uganda was where his heart was and that he had absolutely no intention of ever returning to Italy. Maybe that was also why Jonathan called the mission station The Heart because it was indeed where Giuseppe had invested his heart for the past 40 years.

He was a spiritual refugee and a true revolutionary. As I got to know him I remember thinking that if Jesus had ever met him he would surely have thought that he was living the faith in exactly the way He had intended it to be lived, rather than in the way that Christianity has been twisted to serve political and economic ends.

As I drove Sambana and Jonathan to the mission in Alex's Land Rover, Jonathan made it clear to both of us that he'd still prefer Sambana to leave the country. In contrast to Jonathan continuing to want Sambana leave, she'd turned me round to her way of thinking.

I figured that if she was in a safe location, but close enough for me to regularly see her and our baby when it was born, that had to be better than our being separated and unable to communicate. That wasn't something either of us wanted and the question of whether I should leave the country with her never really crossed my mind. I just took it for granted that I should continue playing an active part in the civil war for our combined futures.

Like Giuseppe, I felt my heart was in Uganda. It was where Sambana wanted to be and I didn't consider us making a life together anywhere else. Though he still wanted Sambana to leave the country, having taken on the role of father that had passed to him on his brother's death, Jonathan now seemed to be really looking forward to becoming a grandfather. He seemed at once happy, excited and nervous.

Arriving at the mission station at dusk I had an eerie moment of déjà vu. The small community was organized in a similar way to Alex's village, which, though a common layout in Uganda, brought back uncomfortable memories. The appearance of two kindly looking men, on the steps of the house

Jonathan had told me to pull up in front of, quickly allayed my sudden apprehension.

Tall, clean shaven, grey-haired and with gentle eyes framed by a wise-looking face, Giuseppe's presence inspired calm and tranquillity. He was accompanied by a Ugandan priest in his thirties, who Giuseppe introduced as John. Like Giuseppe, John had a soft kind face; a small, flat nose and full lips, closely cropped hair, a smooth dark complexion and a warm welcoming smile.

That evening, as we ate dinner in the mission house's dining room, Jonathan, Giuseppe and John discussed the changing political situation in Uganda. During the past few months, Obote's presidency had been falling apart at the seams. This was being reflected in what was happening in the army. All Obote's energy had gone into trying to eradicate opposition to his government but with a bankrupt economy, a fragmenting army and a fractured powerbase, it looked as if his days in power were numbered.

Two distinct ethnic groups, the Acholi and the Langi, dominated the military. Conflict between these groups in the army's upper echelons was splitting it down the middle. Though it was clear Obote had completely lost his grip on the situation, nobody was celebrating. I said I understood why people weren't jumping up and down toasting Obote's imminent collapse, but why, at least, wasn't there a bit of joy – looking at what could be the end of the war.

'If only things in Uganda were that straightforward,' Giuseppe replied. 'Though Obote may fall there are others close to him who'll fight to take his place. We've lived in tyranny for the last fifteen years. It's not that easy for people to, as you put it, jump up and down.'

'The wolf may simply change his clothes,' Jonathan added, 'and, as the pack goes for each other's throats, the hyenas are free to roam.'

Despite Sambana's confidence in an eventual victory, I began to understand why Jonathan was still keen for her to leave the country.

Though it looked like Obote was going to fall, the war was far from over and the chaos on the ground could well intensify. One of Jonathan's main objectives was to know exactly who was active in the area in which his unit was operating: whether government, bandits or armed militia – or all three. The regular patrols he sent me out with seemed to be as much about intelligence gathering as anything else.

Trying to delineate the situation along lines of good and evil was far too simplistic. In a country made up of a number of distinct ethnic groups, where its leaders always seemed to serve the interests of the groups they and their cronies were drawn from or aligned with, the situation was never going to be straightforward. As Jonathan had said to me when I was in the hospital tent, his world was not black and white.

Maybe my original motivation for getting involved had been naïve, though I still believed in my commitment to making a stand and choosing a side. It was that choice that had led me to Sambana and I still believed I had chosen the 'right' side. Despite the violence I'd witnessed and been part of, perpetrated by that side, the people I was fighting alongside had not come to this lightly.

It was about survival, and with the political situation in Uganda in even greater turmoil it looked as if that fight for survival could become even more intense.

EIGHTEEN

A low crescent moon and two thin slits of light, thrown by the Land Rover's Scotch-taped headlamps, were all we had to light our way, as we followed a rough track along a dried-up river bed. With the barrel of his AKM resting on the vehicle's instrument panel, Jonathan rode shotgun in the passenger seat.

Moving his head from left to right, his eyes swept the bush on either side of the track like radar. In the rear, from behind the barrel of his AKM, Heile covered the back of the Land Rover with his own radar-eyes; watching for telltale signs of movement in the scrub receding behind us. We were on our way to Sudan to make contact with Moscow, the leader of a unit of SPLA fighters, just over the Ugandan border.

Beginning a couple of years after Uganda's civil war started, Sudan was in the throes of its own civil war. Though complex, and with a history that far pre-dated the current conflict, in simple terms it was a war between the country's north and south; the south fighting for independence from the politically dominant, economically unfair and dictatorial north.

The SPLA, or Sudan People's Liberation Army, was fighting for an autonomous state but, like the NRA in Uganda, it was made up of a number of different factions and ethnic groups.

Though they'd united to fight the northern government, conflict between these groups occasionally erupted.

A breakdown in one of those sometimes-fragile alliances had left Moscow's unit out on a limb and, because their supply chain had involved a faction they were now in conflict with, they were running low on munitions. Jonathan described Moscow as a brother-in-arms. Heile also knew him. They'd met in an SPLA training camp in Ethiopia and it had been through Moscow that Heile had ended up in Jonathan's unit.

Heile had been a warrior since he was a teenager. He was a Falasha turned Rasta, who'd been brought up by nuns in an orphanage outside the Ethiopian capital Addis Ababa. He'd joined the army at the age of 14 where he learned his skills as a mechanic. He deserted a few years after Heile Selassie died, or was assassinated as Heile claimed, and was press ganged into the SPLA soon after. Despite being virtually forced to take up arms with them he didn't seem to hold any grudges: neither toward Moscow nor Jonathan.

Like my original motivation for seeking out the guerrillas in Uganda, Heile believed in the causes he was fighting for. He and I shared another similar character trait; we both believed in a destiny that was taking us to where we were supposed to be.

When I told him about världsalltet and my idea of The Great Flow, he immediately understood what I was talking about. We both agreed that destiny, and The Flow, doesn't always carry us to places where we might want to be even though, according to our life's philosophy, it might carry us to where we're supposed to be.

'You're here with us now, brother, because you listened to your heart and you followed your soul. That's righteous. It's your Flow, man.'

Heile didn't think there was anything misguided about my being in Uganda. He totally understood why I'd gone there.

'People like you and me are never going to follow the path of the many – that's the way of man. We're on a spiritual journey.' Heile was a deep and thoughtful person with a kind heart.

Our route to Moscow was taking us through Uganda's north-eastern corner and Karamojong territory.

Occupying land running along Uganda's north-eastern borders, and similar to the Maasai in neighbouring Kenya, the Karamojong's livelihood mainly involved cattle. They weren't interested in adopting Western ways and like Pole's people – the San – had their own approach to life that was often at odds with the ways the powers-that-be thought people should be living. Successive governments had tried to exert some kind of control over the warrior-like and proud people of the region.

The Karamojong were pretty much seen as a law unto themselves. Their tendency to do their own thing, including their propensity for cattle rustling, didn't make them particularly popular. The military had been very active in Karamoja during the years before the civil war, and even during it: displacing people and depopulating whole areas.

Jonathan had made a point of keeping his eye on what was happening in the region, as part of his intelligence gathering in the areas around his camp and, more recently, Giuseppe's mission station. I'd scouted around their land with Pole a few times and the elders in various clans in Karamoja knew both Jonathan and Pole. Even so, it felt a bit like we were trespassing, so we were on our guard.

As well as keeping a look out for potential threats, Jonathan and Heile were also looking out for landmarks that would lead us to a Chevrolet Blazer, parked and hidden in the bush alongside the track.

Due to the problems Moscow was having with his supply chain, Jonathan was hooking him up with a couple of men who'd be able to deliver the weapons and ammunition he needed. Slipping over the border from Kenya, they'd arranged to rendezvous with us along the track, from where we'd go into Sudan together.

As we approached a sharp dip in the track, Jonathan reached over and flashed the headlamps' narrowed beams three times before telling me to slow down. He directed me along a cleft in the track that seemed to lead into the scrub.

Low-lying thorn bushes scraped along the Land Rover's pockmarked and battered sides as the fork we'd taken narrowed briefly before opening into a clearing. In the dim light of the crescent moon and the sharply focused beams of the Scotch-taped headlamps, I spotted the silhouette of a pick-up truck against the low trees and scrub on the far side of the clearing.

Jonathan indicated for me to stop, slowly opened his door and got out. From behind the Land Rover I heard a strong South African accent greeting him cheerily.

'How you doing, bloke?'

Heile clapped his hand on my shoulder. 'Come and meet East Africa's Batman and Robin,' he said, as he followed Jonathan out of the Land Rover.

I turned off the engine and got out. Two men were standing in the gloom of the narrow track along which we'd entered the clearing, obviously having followed us in when we'd taken the fork.

'Well met by moonlight, gentlemen,' Jonathan said in his best Shakespearean English.

'You took your time getting here, as usual, you old bugger, but good to see you nonetheless.' The other man replied. From his accent I guessed he was a white Kenyan.

'You know Heile,' Jonathan said, nodding in his direction. Introducing me, he added: 'And this mad Swede's called Lucky.'

Both men were heavily armed. The South African was in camouflage while the Kenyan wore khaki shorts and a shirt. With magazine straps criss-crossing their chests, both seemed to have the air of the desperado about them.

Six-foot plus and with a short Mohican haircut, Cape was in his thirties. He'd met Pole while serving with the South African Reconnaissance Commandos. The fact that he'd been in the South African military at the height of apartheid, but that he'd known Pole and they'd maintained a connection since suggested he was a bit different to the majority of Afrikaners. At the same time he was about as simple as they come in terms of his views on life.

More and more I was seeing the world in all its hues and realizing that the way things appear more often than not has more to do with our interpretation than with the way they actually are. I still wonder if Cape was the guy Pole had taken to Jonathan's field hospital in Botswana. It would make sense if he was.

Scotty was a white Kenyan with a squat and stocky body that had seen better days. He was in his fifties and, at some point in his life, had been a regular soldier. He told me he had various children dotted about the place and also that he'd come from a family of farmers. He talked about getting a stud farm when he made his millions.

Scotty was a good man, with a sense of justice and of right and wrong, but fortune had never really smiled on him. He knew it but wasn't bitter about his lot. I've no idea how long the two of them had been a team but Heile was right, they did make a weird kind of dynamic duo, though maybe as much a desperado Laurel and Hardy as a Batman and Robin.

Scotty and Cape were part of the enigma of war that I was uncovering bit by bit. In retrospect, I guess I was part of that, too. As I was to find out in the years to come, people like them and me weren't peculiar to that particular war. Scotty and Cape weren't exactly soldiers of fortune but their lives were very much based around conflict zones. Nor were they regular arms' dealers, though they could certainly supply whatever weapons were needed.

They were just well connected along both the semi-official and totally unofficial logistical lines that flourished in small, medium and larger theatres of war. Dealing in diamonds and gems across the continent but particularly in East Africa; running guns and taking part as foot soldiers, if they felt strongly enough about the fight being fought. Sometimes they were stage managers, sometimes stagehands and sometimes actors, too.

Introductions over, they led us to the Chevy Blazer and pulled out a box of Tuskers. Handing me a bottle, Cape drew me to the rear side of the Blazer's open back.

'Reckon you can handle that, mate,' he said pointing at a Browning .50 heavy machine gun fixed to a ball joint in the floor of the Chevy's bed and pointing out of its back. 'I'd ask Heile but he's probably stoned and safer up front in the Land Rover than back here with the Browning.'

It was true; Heile did smoke a lot of weed – or 'bango', as he called it. He must have been used to it though because he never actually appeared to be out of it, but it was probably why he always seemed so super-chilled. Pointing forward, an MG3 light machine gun was attached to a roll bar behind the Blazer's cab.

'I'll be on that baby.' Cape said, motioning his Tusker at the gun. 'Any trouble and we'll have it all covered,' he added confidently.

I didn't want to seem like a rookie but I'd never used a Browning before so I had to ask Cape to give me a quick lesson. Far from scorning my lack of knowledge, he was more than happy to show me the ropes and give me all the details about his weapons of choice. By the time he was through, Jonathan had finished briefing Scotty and we were set to leave.

A steel sheet around the Browning provided a protective shield for the gunner and I buckled myself into a waist belt, attached by two leather straps to the top of the pick-up's sides, behind the shield. With Heile and Jonathan leading in the Land Rover we got back on to the track and carried on toward the Sudanese border.

As well as setting up the connection between Moscow and Scotty and Cape, we were also on a reconnaissance mission. Within weeks of Sambana moving to Giuseppe's mission, Obote had abdicated his position and fled the country after Tito Okello, one of Obote's senior military commanders staged a military coup.

Rather than trying to sort out the chaos on the ground, Uganda's new president had simply picked up where the old one had left off by throwing everything he could at the rebels fighting in the bush. He'd even gone as far as recruiting soldiers from Amin's army who'd fled to Sudan when Obote had come to power.

Amin's ex-soldiers were better trained than Obote's but just as prone to terrorizing innocent civilians, and they were coming back over the Sudanese border into Uganda's north as a mercenary army. Giuseppe told us that they'd started to hear the sound of helicopters in the far distance travelling from north to south and possibly coming from Sudan.

If the north-central area had been relatively safer, we weren't so sure it still was. Once again I'd tried to talk Sambana into leaving Uganda, but with barely a month to go till our baby was due and with travel becoming even more risky, I had conceded to her staying where she was. We wanted to gather as much intelligence as we could about troop movements into Uganda and we figured Moscow might have useful information. If he didn't himself, he'd certainly have contacts that could shed some light on what was happening on the ground.

Like a monstrous cloak coming to wrap us in its darkness, the black mass of the Southern Sudanese highlands began to loom closer and closer against the night sky.

Bouncing along the rough track in the back of the Chevy, behind Jonathan and Heile in the Land Rover, I tried to relax my shoulders and soften my knees to better absorb the Chevy's constant dips and rolls. Suddenly the air around us burst into life.

From either side, incandescent needles were flashing toward both vehicles. Following Jonathan's lead upfront, the Blazer jerked violently as Scotty floored its accelerator pedal to pull maximum horsepower from its V8 engine.

Momentarily thrown off balance by the sudden acceleration, but kept upright by the harness around my waist, I jammed down on the Browning's trigger sending a stream of heavy calibre bullets in the direction the tracers seemed to be coming from. Cape followed suit with the MG3: sweeping left and right, firing in long spurts and screaming profanities at our unknown attackers.

The loud clatter of the Browning and rapid tut-tut-tut-tut of the MG3 competed with the clang of rounds bouncing off the Blazer's steeled sides, as the night's stillness suddenly erupted into pandemonium.

A searing burst of pain in my left calf doubled me over and sent the Browning's muzzle skyward. A bullet ricocheting around the Blazer's bed had hit my leg. Still under heavy fire, I gritted my teeth, lifted myself tall and fired back at our attackers, who now seemed to be behind us. A split second later and I was knocked backward, as a cloud of lead shot peppered the Browning's shield, spilled over its protective frame and flayed my chest.

With a sharp cry I dropped like a puppet on slack strings, to be caught by the harness around my waist.

Cape must have been looking at our attackers receding behind us and seen me getting hit because in a flash he was at my side, helping me out of the harness. Lying in the Chevy's bed I struggled to breathe.

'Shit man, if you'd been ducked down behind the Browning you'd have caught it in the face,' Cape shouted at me over the roar of the Blazer's straining engine.

It gave me little consolation as the Blazer bucked and jerked, jolting spasms of pain through my scored chest and punctured leg. Thankfully the vehicles soon slowed to a calmer pace, as we left our attackers behind.

Cape had grabbed the Chevy's emergency medical pack and was doing his best to clean me up. 'Good news is you're not gonna die, mate,' Cape reassured me. 'Bad news is we're not stopping till we get to where we're going,' he added. 'But this'll make you feel better,' he said, emptying the contents of a morphine Syrette into my forearm.

The image of a rough-looking man in the middle of a forest, falling forward onto a pine-needle carpet with his backside up in the air, sprang into my mind as I began to fall into a soft rolling haze.

I have a vague memory of being carried on a stretcher through what seemed like a mine, and looking up at naked light bulbs set at regular intervals in the roof of a tunnel, of being manhandled onto a hard table in a bunker-like room, and of Jonathan's confident hands cutting away the lower leg of my trousers and the bloodied fabric of my shirt.

Jonathan later explained that Moscow's base was in a warren of tunnels and bunkers in the side of a hill, so it wasn't a dream but a brief moment of semi-lucidity before I went under again.

I didn't get to meet Moscow on that occasion but we got the information we needed and Moscow got the connection to the guns and munitions he needed. Following what Moscow had told him, Jonathan also convinced Scotty and Cape to stay with us, knowing how useful their skills and experience were going to be as we tried to deal with the anarchy that was soon to sweep us into its wake.

It wasn't clear who we'd engaged on the way to Sudan. It probably wasn't UNLA but it could have been Karamojong, soldiers from the mercenary units Okello had invited back into Uganda, or even bandit militia from elsewhere in the north. What Moscow had heard though was that since Amin's soldiers had started being mobilized, Karamojong villages were being attacked and looted frequently and having their cattle stolen.

At first they'd thought it might have been their Iteso neighbours in Uganda, or Turkana from Kenya. These groups had been involved in tit-for-tat cattle raiding for decades, and poor rainfall and crop failure in recent years had made it worse. But rather than being taken south, toward Iteso territory, or east, to where the Turkana lived, the stolen cattle were being herded north into Sudan.

What's more, and corroborating what Giuseppe had mentioned, sometimes the attacks on villages involved a helicopter; with attackers flown into the area then supported by firepower from the air.

Moscow was sure it couldn't be SPLA, or any unit that had broken away from them. They were too busy fighting the war in Sudan and didn't have helicopters. He trusted the actions of the Khartoum government less though. Whoever it had been, Jonathan was convinced the situation was getting messier, as those that operated under the cover of war's grey veil took advantage of the prevailing chaos.

NINETEEN

In some respects life at the mission station was definitely easier than life at the camp and, though I missed the bubble Sambana and I had created for ourselves under the flame tree by the river, I appreciated being able to have a slightly more varied diet than fish and root vegetables and a watertight roof over us when it rained.

After all the years of unrest and war, things were hard. There were extreme shortages and obtaining the basics was often a challenge. Like many Ugandans, Giuseppe and John grew their own vegetables and also kept a few goats and chickens. Rice was cultivated in some of the land surrounding the mission, so we weren't going to starve.

One way or another people were doing what they could to survive. A thriving black market in the nearest towns meant goods could be exchanged. Regulated and controlled by the local army units or police battalions, and sometimes the two working together, the black economy was another example of individuals profiteering from people's hardship. Though the powdered milk and machetes we'd seized in the ambush were supposed to be distributed freely, they probably would have ended up being appropriated by the army and sold on the black market, or over one or other of Uganda's borders.

While we were in Moscow's bunker, Jonathan had removed the slug from my calf and the lead embedded in my chest. When we arrived back at the mission station the following night I was still doped-up and groggy.

Sambana was mortified. Being aware of the potential danger does nothing to lessen its impact when it hits you full on, and she hardly left my side for the next few days. She insisted I stay in Giuseppe's infirmary and nursed me with the same care and attention she'd shown when I was in the hospital tent, but now coupled with a lover's intimacy.

It was like a signpost to the recent past of someone I'd once known but had left behind. Sambana's distended belly, carrying the new life we'd created together, signposted the future I'd left them behind for.

Tenderly changing the dressing on my chest wounds a day or two after my return she looked at me through a shadow of pain that was suddenly cast across her face.

'Don't leave me, Lucky,' she whispered; tears filling her eyes. 'I've lost nearly everyone I've ever loved... I couldn't bear to lose you, too.'

Reaching out my hands to cradle her beautifully contoured face I brushed her tears away with my thumbs, as they followed the smooth ridges of her high cheekbones. Gripping my wrists, she dropped the weight of her head into my hands, her tears now spilling over my chest. I imagined them filling the wounds left by the shot and flowing through the permeable membranes of my body's tissue toward my heart; washing away all the pain I'd ever felt.

'I love you Sambana... from the moment I saw you, now and forevermore. You're the reason I came here. Don't you see? I'm never going to let you go.'

I reached out and cupped her round belly in my palms. I felt our baby slumbering in its impermeable membrane. At least for now protected from the deep seam of sorrow that seems to underscore all human life. A solitary tear hung like a liquid seed on Sambana's face, glistening in the morning sunlight pouring through the infirmary's windows.

We were the kernel that held the promise of new life. Uganda was burning, but from its ashes we would rise together.

Our baby was born at the start of the second rainy season, earlier than we expected.

I was at the mission station still recovering from my wounds when she arrived and Jonathan, Pole, Heile, Scotty and Cape were there, too. Scotty and Cape had returned from a second trip to Sudan, where they'd been supervising an airdrop of arms from Tanzania they'd brokered for Moscow and Jonathan. Pole and Heile had been scouting around Karamoja, trying to find out exactly what was going on and who was responsible for the attacks happening there.

We were sitting under a jacaranda tree on a small hill overlooking the mission station, drinking pombe that Pole had somehow conjured up. None of us could get him to admit where he'd got the homebrewed alcohol from and as we were teasing him about his having found himself a lady-friend John's voice rang out, calling me insistently from the mission below. I limped down the hill as quickly as I could; Sambana's waters had broken.

Born with a solitary porcelain-white tooth in her lower gum, we called our beautiful daughter Miss Shinytooth. Within weeks I had her smiling at my silly faces and clowning antics. The tooth meant feeding could sometimes be a bit of an ordeal for Sambana, and I felt for her.

Though Giuseppe had given away a lot of the powdered milk that he'd been hiding after the ambush there was still plenty left, but Sambana refused to use it, saying it was no substitute for what God had given her.

As a way of supplementing people's diets, particularly given the shortages caused by the war, powdered milk came in very useful. A lot of women used it to feed their babies but often with detrimental consequences for the babies' health. I'd heard about the way Western companies were literally dumping the stuff for free across the continent. They were undermining nature's way and attempting to engineer future demand without giving a thought to how difficult it might be for women to make up the bottles using sterile water.

Like most parents, we wanted to be able to do the best we could for our child, and we'd both been fortunate enough to have had an education that had given us some kind of awareness. People that hadn't been so fortunate sometimes didn't have the same insight.

To say I was a doting father was an understatement. The love I felt for my daughter was only matched by the love I felt for her mother. The wound in my calf became a blessing, as there was no expectation that I'd be back out in action until it was properly healed. The rains had also curbed the unit's activity in the field.

I remember those weeks, with Sambana and Miss Shinytooth at the mission station, as a kind of timeless continuum. Miss Shinytooth seemed like a magnet for others, too. Both Jonathan and Pole started spending more time with us. Sambana and I joked with Pole, saying he really did have a secret lady-friend living nearby but he continued to deny it saying he was only there to make sure we were all right.

I think Jonathan wanted to be near his kith and kin, too. After all, having taken the place of Sambana's father, you might as well say he was Miss Shinytooth's grandfather – and if I was the doting father he was certainly the besotted *babu*.

During the day, if I wasn't weeding Giuseppe's vegetable plot or patching up a leaking roof somewhere on the station, I'd take Miss Shinytooth on my back and go walkabout; introducing her to the few children who lived on the station, and feeling so proud at their mothers' admiring smiles.

In the evenings, we'd sit on the terrace of Giuseppe's house, sipping Johnnie Walker by the light of two hurricane lamps and listening to the heavy rainfall drumming on the house's galvanized metal roofs.

If I'd had foresight I might have wondered who the rain could have been signalling to.

Soon after Miss Shinytooth was born, Pole began carving a figurine of a baby in white ebony, and during those evenings he'd either continue to work on that or on three similar figures he was carving in black ebony.

It was a fragile kind of calm though, both the civil and economic situation were going from bad to worse and I don't think there was any corner of the country now unaffected by the war, in one way or other.

Jonathan broached the subject of our leaving the country again but Sambana refused to talk about it and, in the rosy light of our daughter's birth, I'd become caught up in a bubble that carried the illusion of our security.

It was on one of those wet evenings that the ongoing plight of the country's people presented itself at the foot of the steps to Giuseppe's veranda.

Giuseppe, John, Pole, Jonathan, Sambana and I were finishing our evening meal when, through the torrent falling around the terrace, I noticed a figure slowly approaching the house. I looked at Pole. He'd seen it, too. He stood up and walked to the top of the steps, as the figure of a gaunt, drenched and hunched man materialized out of the deluge.

Pole questioned him abruptly and the man replied in a dialect I didn't understand. Pole looked at Giuseppe. 'He's Acholi, can you speak with him?'

Giuseppe walked down the veranda's steps and took the man's hand in a warm welcome and signalled for him to mount the stairs to the terrace. His feet were bare and he was dressed in a ragged T-shirt and frayed, cut-down jeans. He had a khanga tied across his back in which I could see round, grapefruit-shaped objects.

Shivering with cold, he only appeared to have one arm. With his head hung down, he tentatively climbed the steps to the terrace. John pulled an empty chair out from the table and motioned for the man to sit. Keeping his head down he mumbled what I took to be a 'thank you'. John disappeared into the house and the man kept his eyes firmly fixed on the floor.

As water dripped from him, pooling around the legs of his chair, he seemed to exude an air of abject wretchedness. His sudden materialization had completely transformed the atmosphere, as if we'd been abruptly transported into a parallel universe where, though everything appeared to be the same, it was actually the negative of where we'd come from.

I looked from Sambana to Jonathan, both were scrutinizing the man with looks that seemed to combine puzzlement and concern, both for him and for us.

Jonathan and Giuseppe spoke to the man in Acholi. At first he only replied to their questions with simple one-word answers and short phrases before slowly beginning to open up. I couldn't understand what he was saying but it dawned on me, as he spoke, that the feeling I seemed to be picking up from him was one of terror.

Something had completely traumatized the man. The feeling he seemed to be casting over the veranda was both contagious and very uncomfortable. I felt Sambana clasp my hand under the table. Her grip was tight but her fingers had turned to ice.

I think both our jaws dropped when the man lifted his sodden T-shirt, exposing the swaddled form of a small baby in the arm I thought had been missing. He passed it to Giuseppe who immediately rushed it into the house.

Pole asked the man something and he removed the khanga from his back. The grapefruit-shaped objects were coconuts. Jonathan sat back in his chair, shaking his head. Sambana mirrored her uncle, sitting back with a cry and lifting her hands to her mouth. I realized the water now running from the man's face was no longer rain but his tears.

John appeared from the house carrying a steaming bowl of cassava broth and a plate of millet bread. He put it down in front of the man and motioned for him to eat. Looking as if he hadn't seen food for days and as if he was about to say grace to the Almighty, the man covered his face with hands and began rocking his body. John placed a hand on his shoulder and let it follow the man's movements, as he rocked back and forth and sobbed into his open palms.

Standing at the door to the veranda and holding the baby, now wrapped in a clean, dry and warm blanket, Giuseppe signalled for Sambana. She looked at me, displaying a vulnerability in her eyes that I'd not seen before, and tugged at my hand to go with her. We followed Giuseppe to his lounge.

Once in the room Sambana took the baby from the old priest and, with her face hovering over the baby's, started talking to it in a soft and reassuring voice. It immediately started whimpering and nuzzling her breast. She unbuttoned her blouse and, sitting down, began feeding it. Sitting down myself, I looked to Giuseppe for an explanation of the calamity that had just walked into the mission.

TWENTY

As I blithely followed the hand that destiny was dealing, reality seemed to have the habit of catching up with me when least expected.

After Giuseppe recounted the man's story, I seriously began to question my fluctuating commitment and half-hearted attempts to persuade Sambana to leave the country.

Living on coconut flesh and feeding his baby coconut water, the man had taken five days to walk cross-country through the rains to get to the mission station. He'd known someone who'd been treated in the station's infirmary years ago and they'd spoken about Giuseppe as a priest with the kindest of hearts. Not surprisingly, when disaster had befallen the man's village it had been the first place he'd thought of going.

Spitting fire from its belly, an ashen storm with whirling blades had descended from the sky and swept the man's village away in a torrent of blood. Old and young, men, women, babes in arms; there had been no distinction when the tempest had come.

I spoke to Jonathan later. All the man could tell him was that the assault from the air had been followed up with men on the ground. The village's attackers had been made up of a mixture of West Ugandans and Sudanese, and at least three had been white like me.

The attackers had left with everything of value in the village.

The man's story matched what Jonathan had heard during his scouting around Karamoja. It seemed that systematic robbery and extortion was at the root of the terror seeping over the Sudanese border. Jonathan had been told of villages in Karamoja, deserted by people fleeing previous UNLA operations in the area, being occupied by armed units; maybe UNLA, maybe non-Karamojong militia or maybe mercenaries, which sounded like the group that had attacked the Acholi man's village.

Wanting to understand exactly what was going on and who was involved in the new wave of anarchy sweeping the north, and to run-out whoever seemed to be trying to move into Karamojong territory, Jonathan proposed a search-and-destroy mission that would take the fight to whoever was adding to the growing chaos.

As I watched the man's baby feeding at Sambana's breast, and heard the compassion in Giuseppe's voice as he spoke, I wondered at the paradox of our human potential.

How was it that we could love and hate in equal measure; that we could be capable of such selfless caring and such awful cruelty? How was it that we could shine with such brilliance and still shroud ourselves in the darkest of shadows?

The total spectrum of the palette of being was at our fingertips, waiting for the brush with which we were painting our lives: from moment to moment, day to day, episode to episode. Were we angels at heart, but beasts by nature?

I'd come to Uganda to take a stand against tyranny and oppression and had found the richest love and the deepest sense of belonging. I'd also become an actor in our own tyrannies of violence, staged as competing dramas within the bloody conflict; a voluntary player in war's vacillating grey scale.

Meanwhile, Okello was talking to the leaders of different factions who'd been fighting against the government, trying to put together some kind of coalition government. It could have been an attempt to secure peace but Jonathan was mistrustful and thought Okello was trying to steal victory from under the NRA's nose.

Despite Okello's claim to be pursuing a peaceful settlement to the conflict, the UNLA was still operating outside the control of a coherent chain of command and continuing to terrorize areas of the country to the south of the camp and Giuseppe's mission station. At the same time, the emergence of this new threat from the north introduced another level of peril to the situation.

Jonathan was adamant that peace couldn't come until Okello had gone and that we needed to continue to be proactive amidst all the chaos and confusion. I put every good vibration into The Flow around me; wishing that this would be one of our last missions and that peace would soon come to the war-weary and fractured country. Screened from rebel activity, that up until then had pretty much entirely taken place in the bush, even Uganda's capital, Kampala, was no longer free from the sound of gunfire, as things fell apart.

I really didn't want to leave Sambana and Miss Shinytooth but with my wounds now healed I felt I had to fulfil my commitment to Jonathan as an active fighter and more so, my commitment to helping to bring about an end to the war so that we might start to build the life we'd planned for, in a country at peace.

Maybe remembering how I'd returned after the last mission, Sambana squeezed me tightly: hugging me in an anxious embrace, as we said our farewell. Neither of us had been able to sleep the night before and our lovemaking had been infused with a sense of urgency.

It had overwhelmed my desire to savour those precious moments of intimacy; while we rediscovered, as if for the first time once again, the contours and lines, folds and furrows of each other's bodies. At the height of our passion I imagined the boundaries of our selves giving way and our tissues merging, as cells consumed cells until we disappeared – devoured by a sweet oblivion.

Before we left, I picked up Miss Shinytooth and held her against my chest; my heart pressed against hers. I looked into her smiling brown eyes. Every day she seemed to grow a bit more into the beautiful little person she was becoming. Each day a new look seemed to cross her happy face and a new sound spring from the tiny lips I planted my goodbye kiss on. Sambana took her from me.

'Come back soon, sweetie,' she whispered in my ear, as we enclosed the three of us in our arms.

Jonathan didn't want to take more than two vehicles and six men. He told us that if we encountered too many of the enemy for us to handle we'd come back to the camp for reinforcements.

Driving in the Land Rover with Pole, Heile and Cape, I followed Jonathan, Scotty and Maalik, one of Jonathan's men from the camp, who led the way in the Blazer.

As we speculated on who might be responsible for what seemed like organized pillaging going on in the north, Cape told us about a shady character he'd come across some years earlier, when he'd been involved in training RENAMO fighters, in the early days of Mozambique's civil war. Operating in the country's Tete Province, close to the border with what was then Rhodesia, this individual, known as 'The Colonel', had run an ivory-poaching and human-trafficking enterprise.

Cape said they'd never found out where he was from, but thought he was possibly Mediterranean, Israeli or a light-skinned Arab. The man had used the chaos and confusion created by the civil war as a smokescreen to conceal his operation. He used landmines to injure and maim elephants in the bush and a helicopter gunship to fly in with his crew, hack the tusks from the dead or badly wounded elephants, and fly out again.

He and his gang also used the helicopter as an airborne slave ship. Attacking villages from the air, they'd swoop down and snatch people to sell as slaves in North Africa and the Gulf.

'If you're totally lacking in conscience and you've got no feeling,' Cape shouted as an endnote, over the Land Rover's noisy engine, 'war's hell can be a bad guy's heaven.'

It made horrible sense. If you worked just beyond the frontline, the disorganization and chaos created in the wake of war's shocking violence could be exploited for all kinds of profiteering. I shuddered at the thought of the negative extremes of human potential.

We figured that this was what was going down in Karamoja, maybe being organized by the same people who'd attacked the Acholi man's village or maybe by a different crew. Whoever it was, people were being murdered and their possessions stolen and cattle rounded up and driven over the border into Sudan.

During the previous year the UNLA had been involved in joint operations with the Kenyan army, trying to put a stop to the Karamojong stealing cattle from their neighbours in both Uganda and Kenya. On top of this, armed civilian militias, made up of neighbouring people who'd had cattle stolen, had also been involved in revenge attacks.

Part of the problem stemmed from the fact that the Karamojong worldview put them slightly at odds with other cattle-herding peoples. Pole explained to me that the way they saw it, all cattle ultimately belonged to them. Not so different I supposed to the way others thought they could take people's land, just because it happened to be there without a fence around it. Their rustling got worse during times of drought and crop failure, and it was local food shortages that had triggered the outbreaks, which had led to the UNLA and Kenyan army getting involved.

The military intervention had resulted in whole areas being cleared of people and, during their scouting, Jonathan and Pole had found evidence of cattle being gathered and herded toward Sudan from these areas. The whole of the region had been affected by the chaos generated by the civil wars in both in Uganda and Sudan, and the disruption caused by the UNLA and Kenyan army, and armed militias involved in revenge attacks.

The Karamojong weren't a passive people and would defend their livestock with their lives but, like the man Cape had come across in Mozambique, whoever was behind this wave of banditry was using the general turmoil to hide his operation; running it on the back of people's misery.

The area we were heading toward was predominantly flat savannah, with none of the bush 'garages' that we used to hide vehicles in areas with richer vegetation. Not wanting us to drive right into the thick of the hotspot without scoping it out first, Jonathan suggested we find a relatively concealed spot to park the vehicles and make a temporary camp. From there, Pole and Cape would recce the neighbouring territory to get a sense of recent human and cattle movement.

Basically we wanted to find out where the 'Mickey Mouse', as Jonathan called them, were based in Karamoja and, if he thought we had the firepower, engage them and take them out.

Once in Karamoja we found a spot, off-road, among some low trees and thorny vegetation and waited for Cape and Pole to gather the intelligence we needed. At regular intervals, with a pair of binoculars on top of the Land Rover's cab, we took it in turns to keep a lookout for hostiles.

I could pick out the circular thatched roofs of a couple of homesteads in the far distance. They appeared like tiny grains of cereal in relation to the imposing mass of Mount Moroto, even further in the distance. The mountain's serrated escarpments cut across the horizon, giving a dark and jagged edge to the late afternoon's soft azure sky.

I imagined Pole and Cape, like a pair of bloodhounds, sniffing through the tall grass and low bush; with not a solitary imprint, overturned rock or broken shrub going unnoticed.

It sounded like the Mickey Mouse had been operating with relative impunity and were likely to have become sloppy in terms of the marks they'd leave behind; broadcasting their movements to those who could decipher the signs they left. I was sure Cape and Pole would come back with a detailed picture and full story.

I wanted them to come back soon so we could get this over with. I didn't want to be there. I wanted to be with Sambana and Miss Shinytooth at the mission station.

I trusted Jonathan's judgement and had faith in his strategy, I just wanted to get the job over and done with and go home to my woman and child. I wanted the war to be over so we could all start building our lives anew. I wanted my mother and father to meet Sambana, to be able to hold their grandchild and to be there when we got married. Since Miss Shinytooth had been born all I wanted was for us to build a home together, have more beautiful kids and live the normal life that, as a lifelong outsider, had always seemed beyond my grasp.

Pole and Cape didn't return till very much later that night. After they'd left us they'd picked up the trail of a small group of six Mickey Mouse; possibly a raiding party, possibly a reconnaissance unit. They'd hoped they'd lead them back to their main camp but it seemed as if they weren't ready to go back yet. Whatever mission they were on, it hadn't been accomplished yet.

When the Mickey Mouse had set up camp and bedded down for the night, Pole and Cape had returned.

They wanted to continue tracking them knowing that eventually they'd lead them to the main group. It made sense but there was no knowing how long they were going to take to do that. Jonathan suggested a couple more of our unit join Pole and Cape, to even up the numbers between us and, given that we didn't know how long we'd be scouting them before they led us to their camp, to take the pressure off the two bloodhounds.

I volunteered immediately. I figured I'd be better off keeping active rather than waiting around, brooding about Sambana and Miss Shinytooth. I was glad when Heile followed suit. After Pole and Cape, he was probably the most experienced fighter in the unit and since that first time we'd met, when he'd lent me his cassette player, we'd developed a nice easygoing friendship. We seemed to share the same wavelength.

We set off for the Mickey Mouse unit's camp under the vast panorama of the Milky Way.

As we trekked on foot, I thought about the UNLA unit Pole and I had stalked the first time we'd gone tracking together. During subsequent missions what I'd learned then had gradually become second nature. Even as far back as the time I'd returned to Alex's village with Pole and felt and seen the predator in him, I'd felt it in myself too. But now I knew it; it was the residue of a primordial and feral past that persisted at the core of my human being.

It felt like a foggy memory from the dawn of humankind when the animal was our greater self. I felt I knew very little about this side of me, even though I could look back to when I was a boy and see how, in certain situations, I'd relied on it and sought it for assistance; unconsciously acknowledging it as a part of me with its own awareness and knowledge.

I had a sense of how dangerous and destructive this animal side could be and both feared and felt attracted to it. It was the dark side of my moon: a dim and hidden part of me that I was curious to hold a light to.

Throughout the following day Pole, Cape, Heile and I stuck to the heels of the Mickey Mouse. As the day unfolded and as they scouted-out one village after another, it became clear that the unit was a recce party, scoping the area for a future raid. It was also clear that the locals had stepped up their level of vigilance in the wake of the recent wave of attacks and raids.

From the boys looking after herds of goats to the men herding cattle, everyone seemed to be armed. We even spotted a small 1960s flatbed truck, fitted with an FN MAG machine gun. It wouldn't pack the same punch as a Browning in the back of a Chevy, but it was a step in that direction. If the Mickey Mouse had been used to easy pickings, it looked like those days were over.

The Karamojong were definitely preparing for trouble ahead but I knew it would just up the ante, and that the raiders would attack with heavier arms. One way or other it wasn't intelligence we intended the recce party we were following to be able to act on.

We figured that if we could take out the main camp, and losses began to outweigh profit, maybe the kingpin operating out of Sudan would have second thoughts about his enterprise in Uganda.

As the day drew on I began to wonder if the Mickey Mouse would be heading back to the main camp. We had no idea where it was but I guessed it would be at least a day's hike from the areas inhabited by the locals, and by the late afternoon we seemed to be moving away from the savannah and the herds of skinny-looking livestock.

Maybe we were in for a night hike, which was fine by me. The sooner they took us to their camp the sooner we'd be able to go back for the others and complete our mission; but then the Mickey Mouse ran into the simple homestead of a family, in the wrong place at the wrong time.

TWENTY-ONE

From the cover of the tall grass, surrounding a small circle of huts on a dusty plateau sheltered by a rocky escarpment, we watched the six Mickey Mouse with AKs at the ready, cautiously moving from hut to hut looking for signs of human life.

As if long deserted, most of the huts were in a state of disrepair. A barely lit but still smouldering cooking fire, a raggedy goat tethered to a stake and a few scrawny chickens pecking at the dusty ground, however, suggested the little village was still inhabited; there just didn't seem to be anyone about at the moment.

For the sake of whoever owned the chickens and goat, I hoped they were going to be away for a while and the Mickey Mouse would just take what they wanted and continue on their way.

The men were dressed like civilians in jeans and T-shirts but moved efficiently from hut to hut like soldiers with some training at least. A shout from one of the men in one of the huts drew the others' attention. He emerged grinning, carrying a large calabash. I looked at Pole and raised an eyebrow. It looked like they wouldn't be going anywhere in a hurry, as the man had just found the homebrew.

Withdrawing back from the homestead's perimeter I whispered urgently to the others: 'We've got to find a way to warn whoever lives here not to go into the village.' Pole shrugged his shoulders and smiled weakly, looking at me as if I was a silly and slightly simple child, while Cape refused to meet my gaze.

Heile seemed to understand where I was coming from though. 'If we go back around the village we might be able to head-off anyone coming home further back along the path,' he suggested.

'Sorry bloke, there's no way we can risk compromising our position and the whole mission,' Cape asserted. 'If we do anything other than stay exactly where we are we'll be putting the mission, and our lives, at risk.'

'Come on, man,' I implored. 'You *know* what's going to happen if anyone turns up.'

I tried to convince Cape and Pole that Heile and I could double-back through the bush and intercept anyone coming along the path, which twisted up around the base of the escarpment so was shielded from view; as long as the Mickey Mouse stayed on the plateau among the huts.

'And if anyone you warn is armed and starts kicking off?' Cape queried. 'It could put us all in the shit.'

The sound of a sudden commotion coming from the plateau interrupted our exchange and looking back toward the homestead's perimeter my heart sank. A small group of five people, probably parents, a young teenage daughter and grandparents, had rounded the corner onto the plateau.

A man, who I took to be the girl's father, was gesticulating with an AK he was holding across his chest while standing protectively in front of his family. I couldn't understand what he was saying but from his tone and body language I could tell he was nervous and caught completely off guard by the situation.

Sitting on the ground, on logs and low stools, with their weapons either propped up beside them or carelessly placed on the ground, the six Mickey Mouse were lounging around the calabash in a loose circle in the centre of the huts. The fact that they hadn't posted a sentry suggested either poor training or total arrogance, or a combination of both.

If the man suddenly levelled his rifle at them and started firing off rounds he might take one or two of them out before any of them could get to their gun and hit him. In contrast to the man's highly agitated state they played it very cool, like a pack of hyenas calmly circling in on their prey.

They began remonstrating with the man in Swahili, telling him to relax and bring his family over to join them, and complimenting his wife on the fine ajon she'd brewed for them. 'You must have been expecting us,' one of them quipped.

Weakening their target with a malignant psychology, their disrespect and attempts at subtle humiliation were calculated to intensify the man's agitation. From the way his arms and feet were twitching I could see he was psyching himself up to use his weapon. It was what they'd intended, he was no longer concentrating on them. The man's mental focus had shifted to his gun.

I noticed a Mickey Mouse, sitting on a log directly facing the man, nonchalantly adjust his position and start moving his hand. From the angle of our relative positions I could see only the front of his body but I guessed that he was carrying a pistol behind him in a holster or in the waistband of his jeans.

Sure enough, in a single fluid movement his hand whipped around from his back, pointed over the shoulders of the Mickey Mouse sitting in front of him and fired off a single shot from a 9mm pistol, hitting the man in the chest. The man stepped backward with a start; his face registering disbelief.

A deathly silence seemed to fall over the whole scene as, without breaking the fluid motion that had brought his arm up and around from behind him, the Mickey Mouse rose to his feet and walked forward, pumping more rounds into his dumbstruck victim.

Like dancers in an abominable choreography, as the two Mickey Mouse sitting in front of the shooter parted to let him through, the man's family simultaneously parted as the man was jerked backward under a salvo of bullets.

Transported suddenly, I felt myself suspended above the plateau looking down on the three groups of players in this appalling scene; the family, the Mickey Mouse and, hidden off-stage in the tall grass, a transfixed audience of four.

Time hung emptily in the evening's air as spent cartridges hit the baked ground in a succession of dull chimes until a blood-curdling wail from the man's wife rent the air, forcing the seconds back into motion. Knowing the horror had only just begun, I lay my head on my forearm.

With their rifles in hand, the Mickey Mouse surrounded the terrified family. The woman had fallen to her knees by her dying husband. He was sitting upright, coughing dark clots while more blood oozed from wounds in his abdomen and thorax, as his life seeped away into the compacted red earth beneath him.

The Mickey Mouse who'd shot the man brought the butt of his rifle down on the shoulder blades of the sobbing woman, sending her sprawling into the dust away from her husband.

Planting the sole of his boot against the dying man's back, and with total indifference, he casually pushed him to the ground.

They began herding the grandparents, woman and girl toward one of the huts. Forcing the old couple to the floor against its side, they manhandled the girl and her mother through the hut's door. While one of them stood guard over the grandparents the other five went into the hut.

I turned to Pole as cries of fear and screams of terror

echoed off the rocky escarpment, splitting the air all around us. Pole's face was blank and his eyes glazed over, as if all consciousness had left him and his body was in a state of suspended animation. My head felt like it was expanding, as if it was developing a surfeit of consciousness and I was about to burst.

As the girl's cries of terror turned into shrieks of pain I began to get up. I couldn't stop myself. I couldn't lie there and witness this theatre of barbarity and do nothing. It felt so wrong, as if by not acting I was somehow joining the enemy's troupe in this scene of pure evil. Cape must have been watching me carefully. I think he must have suspected what I'd probably end up trying to do.

Maybe they'd discussed it among themselves. Heile had his AK trained squarely on the guard and the hut, Pole appeared to be zoned out, though I have no doubt would have recovered himself in a flash if necessary. But Cape had been charged with minding me because the very moment I started to lift myself up, my Remington pointing at the guard, he threw himself on my back and kept me on the ground.

I tried to move beneath him but he had me pinned down.

'It's seriously fucked up, soldier,' he said, his mouth close to my ear and his voice low but firm, 'and the only way you'll cope is to cut yourself off from what's going on.'

I remembered what Jonathan had said to me before the ambush, on that first mission: remain detached and don't let what you see get to you. I tried to let my body go limp and regulate my breathing, willing the rage coursing through my body to subside.

'It's okay,' I whispered, 'I'm okay now.' He rolled off me.

'We'll get those bastards, bloke,' he assured me. 'When the time's right, those bastards are ours.'

Maybe Cape was right and that was the way to deal with it. I couldn't make them stop but I could make them pay. I'd somehow learned to deal with the killing, more or less. It was still an issue but also a job that sometimes had to be done. To have to passively witness this level of inhumanity and wickedness was something else entirely.

Jonathan had been right. Thought and feeling could have no place. They got in the way and added another level of jeopardy to an already highly volatile situation.

I looked back at the scene in the homestead. The Mickey Mouse who had been guarding the elderly couple had swapped places with one of the group who had been inside the hut. The new guard was saying something to the couple but his back was toward me and I couldn't hear what it was.

The couple's faces were hanging down toward the ground. The old man was shaking his head, looking like he was replying to the guard. The Mickey Mouse cuffed him hard across the side of his skull. It struck me the guard had been asking where they kept their valuables.

I didn't imagine they had anything other than what could be seen.

A sharp report rang out from inside the hut, followed by the woman's shrieking wail; they'd shot the girl.

A burst of rapid fire was followed by the sound of desperate choking as the girl's mother drowned in the blood that was filling her punctured lungs. I saw the old man's hand slide over the dusty red ground and clasp the old woman's trembling fingers.

The Mickey Mouse emerged, zipping up their jeans and straightening their clothing. They were laughing and joking like a group of merry customers leaving a bar at closing time.

Pointing at the elderly couple with the barrel of his rifle, the guard said something to the Mickey Mouse who'd shot the girl's father; I'd already figured him as their leader. He waved his hand dismissively and walked over to the goat. Two more shots rang out as the guard finished off their killing spree.

Night was settling in by the time they set off with the trussed-up chickens in a sack, the trussed-up goat over one of their backs, a sack of grain and the man's AK.

As we picked up where we'd left off, following them on the move, I imagined how I was going to kill the leader.

TWENTY-TWO

At some point during the night the Mickey Mouse stopped for a few hours' rest, continuing on their way at breaklight. Pole and I kept watch while the other two grabbed some sleep. I didn't want to close my eyes so I sat silently next to Pole, under the darkness of a cloud-covered sky.

I could feel Pole's urge to prowl between the Mickey Mouse's slumbering bodies with his bayonet-saw; probing through the intercostal spaces in their chests for hearts that I doubted were even there.

A cold sense of purpose was flowing in my veins. My previous impatience to return to the mission station had been replaced with a sense of focused restraint waiting to be unleashed in time's due course. It drove me on, as we stalked behind the Mickey Mouse from daybreak to mid-afternoon.

During the two days we'd been following them we'd trekked east and then northwards.

From the changing landscape, as the second day wore on, I could tell we were heading toward the Sudanese border. We'd seen evidence of the movement of large herds of cattle in ground that had been churned up by hooves during a deluge but were now baked into hard troughs and ridges.

We figured we were on one of the routes used by the cattle rustlers and probably heading for a transit station before the border where cattle, driven from different areas in Northern Uganda and possibly Eastern Kenya, would be gathered before being herded into Sudan. From what the Acholi man had told us, it wasn't just the Karamojong that were being targeted and robbed.

The nearer we got to the border the more relaxed the Mickey Mouse became. We guessed they were getting closer to their camp. Their pace slowed and they even stopped to roll a joint, but they didn't seem to be in any kind of hurry to rejoin the main group.

We watched them cross a river that cut across the dirt road they'd been following. A bottleneck in the broad river's course and an expanse of flat rock on the riverbed provided a natural ford. From the tracks on the ground we could tell it was used as a crossing for people, cattle and vehicles.

We suspected the camp lay just beyond the river; with all the cattle they were transporting, their transit station would have to be near to a good source of water. All we needed to be able to do was to get close enough to be able to scope-out important details like the number of personnel, their firepower, the camp's layout, the way it was guarded, its fortifications and weak spots. With this information we'd be able to work out whether we could attack with the others or whether we needed to go back to camp for reinforcements.

I felt that sense of purpose quicken in my veins and hoped Jonathan would give the go-ahead for an immediate attack, whatever the details.

On the other side of the ford, the road snaked up a gentle slope, curving around a bend after about 25 metres. We watched the Mickey Mouse disappear around it from the tall grass on the opposite bank. Frustratingly, it was impossible to see what lay beyond the bend. The river banks and sides of the road were covered by long grass making it a relatively straightforward spot to cover. Crossing the river at the ford would put us right out in the open.

We had no idea whether people concealed in the grass were guarding the camp. Just because the Mickey Mouse hadn't acted in a way that indicated the presence of anyone covering the river didn't mean no one was.

Heile and I both looked to Pole and Cape for their expert knowledge on such things; asking them whether the river looked like it might narrow again, further up- or downstream and offer another place to cross. They contemplated the river's course and rate of flow, looked at each other and shrugged their shoulders. I think we'd tested the limits of their knowledge.

We were probably too eager to check out the camp, return to the others and bring them back to finish the job. After what we'd witnessed the previous evening there would have had to have been a full battalion of soldiers for us not to have wanted to get back there and deal with the unit we'd been following, and all their friends, too.

We decided to risk the crossing. Heile volunteered to go first, doubling back through the grass in order to approach the ford from the road. When he passed us a few minutes later, he had his AK strapped across his back and a huge joint between his lips. What we were doing suddenly felt completely suicidal and from another world.

We should have got Cape and Pole to follow the river in opposite directions to see if either could find another safe point to cross while Heile and I waited, concealed in the tall grass watching for any activity on the road. But we hadn't, and now Heile looked incredibly exposed as he waded through the fast flowing river.

With senses fully alert, Cape, Pole and I watched the opposite bank intently. Heile was a sitting duck and with the imperative of the mission foremost we wouldn't be able to jeopardize it by returning fire if the Mickey Mouse had sentries posted in the grass.

I breathed a sigh of relief as his feet made contact with dry ground on the other side of the crossing and then caught my next breath as three armed men rounded the bend in the road.

Without breaking step Heile continued up the road, blowing clouds of smoke from his joint.

Dropping the relaxed demeanours with which they'd rounded the bend, the men eyed him suspiciously: obviously not recognizing him. One of them unslung the AKM hanging from a strap on his shoulder. Heile was on a tightrope strung across a deep chasm and I wasn't sure how he was going to make it to the other side.

Maintaining a calm and non-defended posture, Heile replied to the questions they started firing at him aggressively. I could only make a guess at what was being said, but they hadn't shot him yet. Heile passed his joint to one of them and appeared to ask him something. He began to casually engage the other two and, minutes later, was walking back up the road with the three men.

I could tell from the way they kept their guns at the ready, and from the way they held themselves, that they were still very much on their guard but they hadn't killed Heile and it looked like they were taking him back to their camp. I wondered if he'd passed himself off as a gun-for-hire, looking to offer them his services. Whatever his story, he'd got away with it for now but had landed in a pit of snakes and there was no guarantee he'd be able to maintain his ruse, or that someone further up the chain of command wouldn't decide to kill him just because they could.

As soon as they'd disappeared around the bend in the road Pole turned to Cape and me.

'Wait here, don't move,' he said before taking off; disappearing into the grass on the opposite bank as soon as he'd crossed the river. War's grey shroud had crept into our senses, confusing our judgement and clouding our reasoning. We should have simply figured the likely location of the camp as soon as we'd seen the Mickey Mouse cross the river, and returned to Jonathan and the others before something bad went down.

Pole was back in less than ten minutes. 'They've taken over a deserted village, maybe 30 to 40 men; some women, maybe children, too,' he said quickly. 'We must go and get the others fast – we run.' I knew Pole could rapidly cover vast distances on foot, and could jog for days on end. Though I'd built up a stamina I'd never have imagined I was capable of, I was still nowhere near Pole's level of endurance. I knew time was of the essence and that Heile's life hung in a delicate balance.

If the Mickey Mouse saw through whatever story he was telling then maybe we would be too late. The sooner we were able to get back, the better chance he'd have of stringing them along. The odds were no longer an issue in any of our minds, and we knew Jonathan would think likewise. More to the point, for me the odds had ceased to be an issue since I'd witnessed the brutal murder of the family in their homestead.

When on a long jog during a mission I'd often find myself trawling my mental library of boyhood memories. On this occasion though, I felt myself being driven by the tortured cries of the mother and daughter in the hut at the homestead. Like an audio-memory, their harrowing screams went round and round my head in a mental loop. If Heile hadn't wound up being taken to the Mickey Mouse camp I'm sure Jonathan wouldn't have wanted to attack without reinforcements. As it was, it hadn't been scoped out properly. All we had to go on was Pole's quick tally and his snapshot of the camp's layout.

It felt strange, like an echo of the way that I'd willed the soldier to see only the baby and not me in the pile of corpses after the attack on Alex's village. There was a part of me that was glad Heile was in the Mickey Mouse camp. It would mean Jonathan would risk what felt like a potential suicide mission. As far as I was concerned I wanted to seek retribution as soon as possible. It was the only way I believed I could exorcise the woman and child's screams from my head, where they'd become lodged.

We'd been running at a steady pace for several hours, night was passing and I was tiring. Cape also seemed to be losing momentum but we both pressed on; pushing ourselves to keep up with Pole, who was jogging as if we'd only just started out. Eventually though, probably feeling we were holding him back, Pole told us to wait while he ran on; assuring us he'd return with the others by the afternoon.

I found it hard to estimate how much further he had to run and, in the darkness of another cloudy night, couldn't see the shapes of hills and distant mountains that might have given me a better clue of our rough location. Without the stars as a guide and source of light, I could only guess how Pole was navigating at that speed. I'd simply been following him blindly. I think Cape had too.

Pole left us camouflaged by bushes, near a broad acacia tree; setting off at twice the pace we'd been running at together. Soon after he left us it started to rain, so Cape and I found a thorn-free bush to burrow under for shelter. But it didn't come to anything. The clouds didn't want to give up their moisture and the air continued to hang heavily with an oppressive humidity.

Drenched in sweat, my clothes clung to my body, which had begun to ache with an intensity that seemed to counterbalance the screams inside my head. I let myself sink into the pain my overstrained muscles were producing that, even if temporarily, seemed to be counteracting the soundscape of rape and murder that was haunting my mind.

TWENTY-THREE

Pole was true to his word. By mid-afternoon he returned with Jonathan, Scotty and Maalik. Jonathan greeted us with a grim and stony face. Though he didn't mention it, he knew it had been our carelessness that had led to the situation we were now in. Similarly, we didn't mention the fact that he hadn't been forced to act as part of the audience, witnessing the horror on the plateau, a role that had clouded our later judgement.

Pole drew the village the Mickey Mouse had occupied in the dusty red earth beneath the acacia tree. I watched and listened in awe, as he delved back into his mental picture time and again to extract information from his impression of the village that would help us plan our attack and rescue mission. It was as if he'd taken a three-dimensional snapshot that he held in his mind and was able to walk around it at will. The man truly had super powers.

From the number of Mickey Mouse Pole estimated were in the camp the odds would be something like 6 to 1 but we had surprise on our side; assuming Heile hadn't been forced to talk. We wouldn't find that out until we were crossing the river or were on top of the camp and by then it might be too late to pull out. None of us dwelt on that as a possibility.

Not wanting to give ourselves away with the roar of their motors, we planned to leave the Land Rover and Chevy hidden in the bush and attack on foot. We all hoped the night would be cloudy again, giving us a cloak of darkness. As we got closer though, it started to rain.

Not as it had during the previous night, when a brief shower had simply teased the parched ground, but as a heavy fall of full drops.

The clouds were finally letting go and that was good for us. The Mickey Mouse would be kept inside and visibility would be further reduced for those on guard duty. Scotty also reckoned we could use the Blazer. If its lights were off and it was driven slowly in low gear, he thought he could get it close enough to the camp to be able to take it in at speed once the attack started; enabling us to use its machine guns and upping the odds in our favour a bit.

We left the Land Rover hidden off the dirt road, eight kilometres from the river crossing, and carried on in the Chevy. With headlamps off, Scotty drove cautiously through the rain. Forked lightning licked at the landscape, as Cape, Maalik and I sat huddled under a tarpaulin in the Chevy's rear, while Jonathan and Pole rode with Scotty, up front in the cab.

The rain came down in sheets; a staccato battery filling the darkness around us, beating down on our tarpaulin shelter like an angry god's drum leading us into battle. I felt my heart rise to match its pace, as I looked forward to the frenzy of violent retribution.

When we were about a kilometre from the crossing we stopped again. Jonathan and Pole left us hidden off the road and went forward on foot for a final recce.

Water was sluicing over the world around us like the deluge that heralded the Flood; while we were the Horsemen of the Apocalypse, taking a stand against the evil that had descended on this tainted land. Waiting for Jonathan and

Pole, we double-checked our weapons. With Alex's Colt .455 holstered at my waist, the Liverpool FC AK strapped to my back and Alex's Remington in my hands, I felt more than ready to meet the odds ahead.

Coming back far sooner than we'd expected, Pole and Jonathan returned having been unable to cross the river. They were unsure whether the Chevy would even be able to make it through the torrent. From the amount of rain that was pouring down I realized that we should have anticipated the surging water level. Gaps were opening in our judgement that I hadn't noticed before.

While Jonathan and Maalik manned the machine guns in its rear, Cape and I walked alongside the Blazer as it crawled through the rain toward the crossing. Looking like Rambo with a Mohican, Cape was carrying an L7A1 machine gun; its ammunition belt draped around his shoulders and over his chest and an RPG strapped to his back.

I was being drenched from head to foot, feeling as if I was undergoing a ceremonial bathing prior to the ritual we were processing toward in the night's darkness; knowing that very soon we'd light up the land with another kind of darkness.

As we got closer to the river I began to hear its roar through the monsoon falling from the sky. When we reached the crossing I could see it was moving at twice the speed I remembered and had risen considerably. With Cape and I back on board, Scotty took the Chevy into the rapidly moving flow.

The river surged around, and up and over the Blazer's wheels. Its tyres struggled to hold their ground as the water rushed and tugged at our ark, threatening to carry away all two tons of the Chevy's weight. The opposite bank remained imperceptible through the deluge until we were virtually on it. I waited for a telltale flash to split the night from the muzzle of a waiting sentry, but the darkness remained intact.

When the Blazer was barely out of the river, Scotty halted; the rising torrent teasing the vehicle's rear tyres. Leaping out, we followed Pole into the waterlogged grass bordering the road and, crouching low, quickly moved up to the brow between the camp and the river.

We needed to act fast. The rain was abating as dawn approached and we no longer had time to scope out the village and make a proper plan. We had no idea where Heile might be, nor what kind of situation he was in.

Pole had said he'd counted 20 to 25 huts and homesteads, but there was no telling in which of these Heile might be. For sure he'd know it was us, as soon as we attacked. We just had to hope he'd keep his head down because Jonathan's idea was to go in and blast away. We were making it up on the hoof and our imperatives had become blurred.

I thought about the Mickey Mouse we'd followed. Picturing the distinctive features of their leader, and the way he'd emerged from the hut on the plateau with an empty smile on his face, I realized what my imperative was. Jonathan opened a rectangular metal case that he'd lugged up to the brow and lifted out a square-shaped, metre-long rocket launcher.

'Cape, take the far side of the village,' he instructed, 'and while I hit the place from up here with this beast, take out the largest huts with the RPG – we'll catch as many of them as we can while they're still inside their huts.' He turned to Maalik: 'You're in the back of the Blazer on the MG3.' And to Scotty: 'I'll make four hits with the M202, after that and Cape's rockets there'll be pandemonium down there. Keep your head low, take the Blazer in and whoever Maalik doesn't mow down... you run down.'

Looking at Pole and then me, he added: 'You two, take opposite sides of the village and thin any bastards out trying to slip through... just don't forget about Heile.'

We caked ourselves in the saturated earth at our feet: smearing wet, deep-burgundy mud over skin and clothing to camouflage ourselves.

As a couple of distant forks of lightning had illuminated the surrounding landscape I'd been able to make out the shape of the Mickey Mouse's camp. Dawn would soon bring the village into shadowy relief, giving Jonathan and Cape all the dim light they needed to choose which huts and homesteads would greet the day in bursts of deadly luminescence.

We separated into the long grass and I snaked my way to a clump of low trees that I'd seen caught in the lightning on the village's westerly flank. It felt as if we might be setting sail in a perforated tub but I didn't care.

I'd hardly slept since we'd watched the Mickey Mouse at work on the plateau and a sense of numbness had settled over me since we'd crossed the river. I kept the leader's image at the forefront of my mind; against a backdrop of cold and vicious cruelty, accompanied by a violent soundtrack of murder and rape. I wanted to purge this land of the iniquity that had befallen it at the hands of those sub-human monsters. They could have no place here with Sambana, Miss Shinytooth and me.

The pitter-patter of rain fell on straw roofs less than 25 metres from where I lay, in a tangle of foliage among the clump of trees on the village's western perimeter. I breathed steadily, waiting for the incendiary rockets from Jonathan's M202 to ignite the village in a storm of fire, and the missiles from Cape's rocket propeller gun to blow apart the mud-and-wattle huts I could see in the shadows of the early breaklight.

Between the huts in front of me, in the centre of the village, I could make out two men by a small fire, sheltering from the now lightly falling rain under a grass-covered canopy. I was amazed that the Mickey Mouse didn't have a perimeter of guards set up around their camp. They must have felt very secure and I figured Heile appearing out of the blue hadn't put them on alert either. I wondered where he was and hoped that Jonathan's M202 and Cape's RPG wouldn't find him.

I noticed the dark shape of someone moving in my direction from the huts in front of me. I lined up the figure in the Remington's sights and steadied my aim. As they got closer, I realized it was a woman with bare feet: naked under a dark-blue raincoat that flapped open as she walked quickly toward me.

She squatted, no more than five metres in front of me and emptied her bladder in a noisy gush. As she finished, with a shake of her hips, the centre of the village exploded in a phosphorescent shower, igniting the roofs of the huts caught in the blast.

Without thinking my finger pulled back on the Remington's trigger and, in the roar of the gun's thunder, the woman was thrown backward as if hit full-on by a steel hammer. Behind her body, flailing in the mud, the village erupted in a paroxysm of fire as Jonathan and Cape unleashed the awful power of their weapons' combined force.

The survivors of the initial barrage began to run wildly into the open and away from the huts that had been set ablaze. The screams of people trapped in the flames split the air around me. Short sharp bursts from the MG3 and a roaring V8 signalled Scotty and Maalik entering the fray.

Light cast by the blazing huts shone through the billowing smoke engulfing the village; turning the scene into a veil of frenzied backlit shadows. Tracers from the MG3 cut through the walls of huts untouched by Jonathan and Cape's rockets; lacerating those caught inside. I scrambled up and switched to the AK.

Suddenly a small group of three Mickey Mouse appeared around the huts in front of me and began using them as cover to return Maalik's fire. Dropping to one knee I held the AK's fore-grip firmly, pulled its stock into my shoulder and on automatic, emptied the rifle's magazine at them, then hurriedly replaced it.

Two more Mickey Mouse appeared, running through the smoke between the huts ahead of me. I levelled the AK at them and with short single bursts brought them both down. Then I saw another, running from the cover of a couple of huts further toward the village's rear.

I aimed and fired, bringing him down too.

The sound of gunfire echoed through the smog that engulfed the scene. My breath was catching in my throat and my eyes had begun to smart. The MG3 had fallen silent but an ongoing firefight from the other side of the village let me know it wasn't over yet. From the rear of the village, the steady chatter of Cape's L7A1 suggested the majority of the Mickey Mouse were running in his direction.

I fired into the village at ghost-like shapes I thought I could see through the grey haze.

Suddenly, remembering Heile, I stopped abruptly but the MG3 took over, once again puncturing the air with an intermittent rattle.

Bent low and training my AK from side to side, ready to fire the instant anyone appeared in my line of vision, I moved toward the hut the three Mickey Mouse had used as cover. Its walls were spattered with blood where the AK's rounds had caught them. The men were on the ground, dead or dying. The torrential rain that had come down during the night, and the slow rain that now fell, had prevented Jonathan and Cape's rocket attack creating a firestorm, but I could feel the heat from the burning huts.

As the sound of gunfire began to diminish an eerie hush started to settle on the scene, punctuated by the crackle and pop of flames consuming damp tinder. Grey smoke billowed into the early morning air and I was suddenly overcome with the feeling that I was the sole survivor of a terrible catastrophe.

I moved back into the clump of trees I'd hidden among. Not wanting to risk being mistaken for one of the enemy, and keeping alert and on guard for any surviving Mickey Mouse, I sat down and waited for the others to appear.

The woman I'd hit with the Remington lay on her back in front of where I was sitting. Her arms and legs were splayed and her raincoat open wide, as if she was offering herself to the heavens above. Light rain dusted her body with a screen of moisture, which seemed to highlight the grey sheen that had settled over her dark skin. Flies had begun to gather around her. I remembered the nausea that had engulfed me in the aftermath of the ambush on my first mission, a long time ago. Catching something moving out of the corner of my eye I swung my AK round.

Jonathan and Scotty were edging cautiously around the village's perimeter, coming in my direction. I called out to them when they were close enough to hear me without my having to raise my voice. Jonathan seemed really glad to see me. He gripped my shoulder warmly but his face looked worn and his voice sounded weary.

'We lost Maalik,' he said bluntly, adding the question: 'Any sign of Heile?' I answered in the negative.

Cape was waiting for us in his position behind the village. Bodies covered the ground beyond the rearmost huts. Thinking the back door their best exit, the Mickey Mouse had run from the MG3 in front of the village into Cape's L7A1 at its rear.

On the village's eastern flank, Pole was surveying the muddy ground around an empty corral. 'Cattle here maybe five, maybe six days ago,' he said, offering us a handful of dung for inspection. We all declined.

'Did you see Heile?' Jonathan asked him. He shook his head.

Grabbing my arm, Pole said: 'Come, I'll show you something make you happy.' He led me away from the corral and further up the village's eastern side to the solitary body of a man, lying on its side in a patch of scrubby grass by a narrow path bordered by low trees and bushes. Getting closer I noticed pink coils of fleshy tubing protruding from his abdomen.

'Mickey Mouse leader,' Pole said, proudly.

Pushing his boot under the contorted mask that had been his face, Pole lifted the eviscerated man's head. Fear and horror were imprinted on it: the emotional signature of his death. I studied his features closely.

'That's him all right,' I said, nodding at Pole. 'How'd he end up losing his guts?'

Pole went through a pantomime demonstration of how, when Jonathan and Cape had started firing their rockets, the man had come running out of the village toward the bushes where Pole was hiding. Recognizing him immediately, Pole had stepped out from where he was concealed and sliced the man's abdomen with his bayonet-saw. It had been a simple, almost clinical execution. I felt slightly disappointed, as if Pole had robbed me of my rightful prize.

Jonathan, Cape and Scotty joined us and we carried on around the village till we were standing by Scotty's Blazer. Maalik's inert body lay on the Blazer's bed, covered by the tarpaulin we'd sheltered under from the rain. Someone firing from the village had hit him and I wondered if it had been one of the three Mickey Mouse that I'd killed.

'We'd better look for Heile,' Jonathan said, almost reluctantly. I understood why.

We'd hit the village with such ferocity, nothing in it was now moving. It had been a crazy plan, if you could even call it a plan. Jonathan was tired; above all he was tired of the war. I knew I was, and it felt as if I'd been in it only for a short while. We were no longer thinking straight.

As we started looking through the debris we all feared the worst. Knowing the leader of the Mickey Mouse recce unit had been dealt with was no consolation for the fact that it looked like we'd lost Heile. As we moved through the smouldering village, the weight of the realization that we'd somehow approached this all wrong pressed down on me.

The smell of seared flesh hung in the grey haze clinging to the air surrounding us; turning the early morning of this new day into a stale and gloomy twilight. Here and there, disembodied hands, arms, legs and feet littered the ground; lying among bodies that had been cut down by rounds fired into the burning village.

I figured that those who hadn't been killed instantly by our bullets would have succumbed to the thick, choking smoke from the flames. Inside burnt-out huts the charred remains of men and women, caught in their sleep, lay baked and burned; covered by ash and cinder. It was a scene of carnage and slaughter from war's grey zone.

It was strange, in death the enemy seemed to have recovered their humanity; no longer Mickey Mouse, just dead people – victims of a terrible circumstance.

Despite combing the village numerous times there was no sign of Heile. We searched the bush surrounding the village, fearing the Mickey Mouse may have killed him the previous day and dumped his body for wild animals to feed on.

In some ways it was a relief. I'd expected to find him among the bodies in the village, cut down by our weapons, or asphyxiated by smoke in a hut while waiting for us to pull him out. But it was as if he'd never been there.

We drove back in silence to the spot where we'd left the Land Rover and buried Maalik's body in a grave for an unknown soldier. Softened by the rain, we were able to dig into the ground deeply enough to prevent hyenas from scratching away the earth and disinterring Maalik's corpse.

None of us spoke as we took it in turns to attack the ground, each knowing it could have been any one of us on the receiving end of that bullet. I remembered how Sambana had reacted when I'd returned from Sudan, wounded in my chest and leg. In a firefight death is only ever a hair's breadth away, brazenly flaunting its presence: maybe so too in life, always at our shoulder but surreptitious and covert.

I wondered if Sambana would be worrying about me and suddenly felt a desperate need to get back to the mission and hold her in my arms. I wanted to see my daughter again; to reaffirm my belief in the promise and hope that new life brought as its gift to the world. I needed to feel the salve that love could bring; cleansing me of the grey, and bringing me back from the twilight I felt I'd entered.

As I rode in the back of the Land Rover behind a silent Jonathan and Pole I imagined a world without war. I imagined Miss Shinytooth as a young girl and then as a beautiful young lady. The face of the girl on the plateau came into my mind and I knew I had to take my daughter and Sambana out of Uganda, at least until there was a situation that was approaching stability.

The madness of living in the midst of anarchy, hoping everything would be okay, hit me. Even if just over the border in Kenya with my parents, I had to get Miss Shinytooth, and hopefully Sambana too, out of war's insanity. Nothing was predictable, anything was possible. With death always at our shoulder, things could turn at any moment. I wondered what had held me back before because I suddenly felt ready to insist on their leaving, at least my daughter, if Sambana refused. I knew this time I wouldn't take 'no' for an answer.

Having made the decision I immediately felt easier in myself. Relaxing for the first time in days, I drifted into a deep sleep as the Land Rover rocked and bounced along the bush road leading us back to the mission.

It was Jonathan's cry that woke me, cutting through the oblivion of a dreamless sleep.

Springing upright in my seat, I instinctively grabbed the rifle propped between my legs. An animal-like wailing, pushing up from the depths of his being, pulled me abruptly back to full consciousness.

Jonathan was leaping from the Land Rover. Night was falling. We were outside Giuseppe's house. Pole was hurriedly exiting on his side of the Land Rover and a bitter scent was wafting through the open door.

I pushed at the door in the back and stumbled out. A cold and unnatural stillness hung over the mission station. My legs began to shake as I came around the side of the Land Rover and saw Jonathan bent over a body on the steps to Giuseppe's veranda.

I was moving through a frozen landscape. An arctic chill had enveloped my body. The Earth had stopped rotating on its axis and time had come to a standstill. I struggled to reach the steps through a sullen gloom that cast the world in deep shadow.

Sambana's body lay shattered: angled downward above a trail of blood that had coagulated in a dark pool at the foot of the steps. Partly on the steps, partly on the veranda, her left arm reached out to her side at a contorted angle. Her rigid fingers grasping for the dead body of Miss Shinytooth lying face down on the darkly stained, teak floor of the veranda.

Sambana's lifeless eyes were looking upward through a gaping hole in the veranda's roof at the unfolding night sky where the Milky Way was beginning its endless procession across the heavens. I dropped to my knees and screamed at the twinkling jewels overhead, my tears falling over her hollow shell.

I caught Sambana's body up into my arms but it felt empty, like it belonged to a broken doll. I cradled it against my chest, pressed my face against its vacant mask and rocked it in my arms but Sambana wasn't there anymore.

As I screamed at the stars above I knew she was already too far away to hear me; already lost among their throng, processing into infinity, taking Miss Shinytooth with her and leaving me behind.

So many stars, where were *they*?

Slumped on the veranda, Jonathan held Miss Shinytooth, the granddaughter he'd known for just a while, his tears running over her little face.

Kneeling on the ground before us, his eyes brimming over, Pole completed our tableau of grief.

We'd lost them. We'd left for a while and they'd gone forever to join the stars in their endless procession to infinity.

Part 3

ONE

In the singularity of that moment a line was scored across my life. There was time before I found Sambana and Miss Shinytooth dead and there was time after.

I was picked up by an almighty wave and cast so far from where I thought I'd been going I had no way of locating myself. A huge and heavy door clanged shut; cutting me off from who I had been and sealing me into a future landscape that bore no resemblance to anything I'd anticipated.

Frozen in the twilight realm I'd been sucked into during the days before that moment, and with the healing essence of love's salve dashed away, I was as lost on Earth as Sambana and Miss Shinytooth were among the myriad stars on high.

For Jonathan and Pole, too, realizing The Heart had become part of the continuum of violence and destruction shattered the dream we thought we'd been fighting for.

Scotty and Cape found us locked in our scene of despair; it could have been hours or just minutes after we'd arrived at the mission station, I have no idea. They also found Giuseppe in the living room of the house, on the floor beside an upright chair, with a single gunshot wound to his head.

John had been shot in the kitchen at the back of the house and they discovered the Acholi man with his throat cut in the

239

mission station's infirmary. His baby's broken body lay on the floor in the corner of the room, as if it had been hurled against the wall.

In a clearing, just beyond the station, they discovered the telltale signs of a helicopter having landed. Of the handful of women and children who lived on the station, there was no sign – except for one child. The hole in the veranda's flimsy roof, through which it appeared Sambana and Miss Shinytooth had fallen, told the story of what seemed to have taken place.

The sole remaining child filled in the gaps and gave us the background that had led to the calamity.

In that background, in the shadows of war's grey realm, the spectre of characters like the man Cape had come across in Mozambique were lurking; feeding off chaos and exploiting a ghastly flaw in the nature of man.

Like forensic detectives at the scene of a crime, Cape and Scotty pieced together a jigsaw that seemed to match the story the Acholi man had told us. Except that rather than slaughtering everyone, the women and children had been snatched and taken away in the helicopter to an unknown fate.

Cape and Scotty surmised that Sambana had jumped from the helicopter with Miss Shinytooth, fearing that they were going to become victims of an atrocity like the one we'd witnessed on the plateau in Karamoja. I listened to them telling their version of what had happened but I wasn't really there, and their words drifted around a cold void. My shell was as empty as Sambana's body felt.

As for the child that had been left behind, Jonathan found him at death's door in the underground storehouse in which Giuseppe had hidden the contraband we'd seized during the ambush. The store had been used throughout the war to hide weapons, supplies, spare parts for vehicles; whatever the rebels needed hidden in a place it was unlikely anyone would ever think of looking.

It was many days before the boy was able to tell us his version of what had happened. By then I was on a path to terminal self-destruction; drinking myself into a perpetual, alcohol-induced oblivion.

It was the boy, and his attachment to me over the weeks that followed us finding Sambana and Miss Shinytooth, that eventually pulled me back from the edge, and his caring for me in my darkest moments that turned me from being a victim of circumstance into an agent of my own destiny once again.

Jonathan discovered him in the store while the rest of us were digging graves for Giuseppe, John, the Acholi man and his baby. The people who had carried out the raid on the station had ransacked it. The boy was lying in his own vomit; desperately dehydrated, barely conscious and covered in powdered milk. We later discovered that he'd been force-fed a container of powdered milk before being shut up and left to die in the dark-as-pitch and airless store.

I recognized him as one of the children I'd see playing around the mission station. I remembered helping him sail a little boat in a large puddle of rainwater. He'd told me his father had made it for him. I later found out his father had been killed in the war. The boy had been so curious about Miss Shinytooth; wanting to know if she was my baby – talking to her and making her smile and giggle.

The story he finally told was as desperate as it was pathetic; adding to the futility of the deaths of Sambana and Miss Shinytooth, and the others. What he'd been coerced into doing had led directly to the mission station being targeted, but he was an eight-year-old child. None of us harboured any sense of recrimination toward him.

If anyone should have been blamed it was his mother, but then she was just trying to do what she thought she could to get her and her son out of the situation in Uganda, and she'd ended up being taken away in the helicopter along with the other women. Maybe it was a responsibility we all needed to share.

Even for the few of us that knew about the store, Jonathan and Giuseppe had always been very careful to keep its exact whereabouts a secret. Giuseppe may have told John but, for the very reason that led to what had happened, he wouldn't have wanted anyone else knowing about it.

Unfortunately, and by accident, the boy's mother found out, and the consequences were as dire as Giuseppe had feared. Late one night she'd watched Giuseppe going into the store and had then managed to get into it herself. She'd taken some cartons of powdered milk and machetes, given them to her son and told him to take them to sell in the market in one of the towns in the region.

The boy said his mother hadn't wanted to do it, and had told him that she knew it was a sin, but she wanted to get out of Uganda and take him to Kenya and for that she needed money. With his father dead, she feared for their future in the country.

The bus the boy had taken to the town was stopped at a police checkpoint, and when it was searched the police had found the milk and machetes. They'd beaten the boy and even dragged the innocent woman he'd been sitting next to off the bus and beaten her, too, assuming she was his mother.

Individuals in the police and military were so tied into the circulation of goods on the black market. Inevitably someone wanted to know about the boy and where he'd got hold of more machetes and powdered milk than a regular member of the public should have access to.

Somehow word had got back to the unit with the helicopter. Maybe they were working with the police. Maybe they'd become the main players in the region's black market. Either way, the police had forced the terrified boy to tell them where he'd got the milk and machetes, and then tied him up and put him in a sack.

He told us how he'd been taken from the police compound and flown to the mission station in a helicopter. He said they'd kept him in the sack until they'd taken him into the store, from where he'd heard shouting, women screaming and children crying but he hadn't seen or heard his mother. He said he hadn't heard shooting, which made us think that a unit had gone in on foot ahead of the helicopter, mirroring what had happened when the Acholi man's village had been attacked. It seemed highly probable that it was the same group.

That people could be profiting from other people's misfortune and suffering, heaping even more misery on top of that with which their lives were already blighted, filled me with a current of anger that intensified the storm already raging within. When I heard the boy's story, I felt the ideals I'd believed in so strongly and that had brought me to Uganda in the first place, explode into shards all around me, becoming tarnished fragments of a broken dream.

The storm began to brew as we tried to deal with the practicalities of the situation at the mission station. Jonathan wanted us to bury Sambana and Miss Shinytooth in The Heart but I didn't. There was somewhere else I thought far more fitting as their final resting place and there was no way I wanted to think of their bodies lying in the same place that had witnessed their cruel deaths.

Urging us to come to a decision quickly and to leave the station as soon as possible, Cape and Scotty became the arbiters of lucidity amidst the trauma that had overwhelmed us.

I argued vehemently with Jonathan and finally persuaded him that we should take the bodies with us. As we argued, I could feel a restrained fury directed at me and realized that there was a part of him that blamed me for the death of his niece and our baby. It made me aware of the guilt and self-recrimination I was already harbouring, and that threatened to pull me down even further.

I struggled to suppress it as I laid their bodies on the bed of Scotty's Blazer, snapping bitterly at Jonathan when he tried to help me. But sitting with them in the back of the Blazer on the way to the camp I was hit by a tidal wave of guilt and remorse.

Our lives, and those of the people whose lives turn within our orbit, are defined as much by the choices we fail to make as they are by the choices we actually make.

I imagined a parallel universe in which I'd been more insistent with Sambana about her leaving Uganda and another in which she'd freely chosen to leave the country. I imagined a universe in which both Sambana and I had not agreed to Jonathan's plan that she relocate to Giuseppe's mission and another in which I'd stopped myself from playing dice with our lives and our futures.

From head to foot I felt the ants I'd seen feeding from the viper in the forest as a child digging their teeth into me.

As the Blazer bounced along the bush road I rocked back and forth in a knot of anguish and self-recrimination. My skin felt as if it was crawling with a multitude of ferocious ants swarming over me, tearing at my flesh.

The weight carried in the choices I'd made, and in my inability to act, seemed to tip the scale of responsibility toward me. I felt myself crumple and fall into the maw of my shadow; tumbling into a heart of darkness as the winds howled and the ants fed.

TWO

Jonathan took the boy to Mama Palma Vini as soon as we arrived back at the camp. He was going to live but badly needed to be cared for.

I couldn't face Jonathan. I blamed myself and I blamed him. Just as he blamed himself and blamed me.

I gave him enough time to leave the duka before making my way there; desperate for the relief Mama Palma Vini's liquor might bring. Moto was still living at the duka, helping Mama Palma Vini run her enterprise, but I was no longer interested in people and their stories, only in doing what I could to cloud the memory of my own.

The camp's population was very much depleted; a large number of its personnel having returned to the south to take part in the NRA's final push for victory. I didn't allow it to register at the time but later acknowledged how even more bitter these wider events made our tragedy.

When we returned to the camp, the war was in its last throes, at least officially. Rebel fighters were storming Kampala and the UNLA were on the run. Within weeks Okello would flee to Sudan and Museveni would take over as President of an exhausted and broken country.

But the stability that the end of the war brought to large areas of Uganda didn't extend to the country's north. As the UNLA fell apart, and its predominantly Acholi soldiers began to flee back to their northern homelands, the inter-ethnic conflict and hatred that had brought about Obote's fall reared its head again. As the soldiers left the south they looted villages, particularly in Langi areas, attacking and murdering their inhabitants as they returned to the north.

During the months following their victory, the NRA followed the fleeing troops and occupied the country's Acholi-dominated northern region. Meanwhile, soldiers that had remained loyal to Okello regrouped over the border in Sudan as the Uganda People's Democratic Army, and started attacking the NRA in Uganda.

The backdrop of continuing instability and unrest gave freebooters, like the unit that had attacked the Acholi man's village and the mission station, the perfect conditions in which to operate. The war I'd come to Uganda to play a part in might be over, but the fighting continued.

We were exhausted and broken ourselves; the bottom had dropped out of my life and I no longer had anything to live for.

When we'd left the mission station Pole had taken off into the bush, saying he'd make his own way back to the camp. I wasn't sure I'd see him again and at that point we still had no idea what had happened to Heile. I was on my own, slowly drowning in a calabash of Mama Palma Vini's alcohol.

I buried Sambana and Miss Shinytooth under the flame tree on our platform by the river, the night after we'd found them at the mission station. I'd laid out their bodies in our hut when we'd arrived back at the camp earlier in the day and then sat on the platform, drinking liquor until the sun went down behind the flame tree.

As the day drew toward its close, the fishermen from the village upstream began returning home with their day's catch, watched by crocodiles basking in the late afternoon sun on the river's opposite bank. A rock had appeared in the middle of our river and I hadn't been there to save my family from the hungry crocodiles. For some, life went on as it had done before, but mine had stopped abruptly and I'd become lost in a veil of shadows.

As I dug into the red earth under the flame tree, a yellow-tinted full moon stared impassively down. Gossamer thin clouds drifted across a clear night sky and I wondered if Sambana and Miss Shinytooth would be able to see me but I avoided looking up at the stars; they were all so far away. I dug until my head was swimming, my arms were numb and my hands were swollen like pumpkins.

I covered the floor of the grave with a mattress of leaves and branches, carried Sambana and Miss Shinytooth out of the hut and laid them on the platform; putting off the moment when I placed them in the enclosed and darkened space of their tomb. The bright moon and starlit sky cast a silver luminescence over their peacefully resting bodies and I longed to join them in their eternal slumber.

When I knew breaklight would soon be approaching I gently laid Sambana on the grave's leafy bed, placed Miss Shinytooth in her arms so they'd be close together for eternity, then covered them with a quilt of jacaranda. As I filled the grave I felt myself burying a dream that had vanished into thin air; so fleeting and short-lived it felt as if it might never have been. I had nothing left to live for and I wanted to die.

Jonathan was lost in his own purgatory of self-recrimination and we didn't speak. Later we fought; a bitter and raging fistfight that took us out of our torpor and propelled us deeper into the grey realm we'd become lost in.

Heile and Pole returned to the camp together.

During the night, under the cover of the deluge, Heile had slipped out of the Mickey Mouse camp and crossed the border into Sudan. He'd made his way to Moscow's base with the intention of discovering who was behind these tentacles of wickedness reaching into Uganda. Pole had left the mission station with the same intention. Their paths had crossed at Moscow's. The information they brought back set us on a course that took us deeper into the grey; but that's another story.

In that boat on the lake with my daughters my thoughts were of their sister; now a twinkling jewel travelling across the heavens with her mother.

This is our story: a moment appearing in time that was lost before it could bloom into the fullness it deserved.

THREE

We measure our lives from moment to moment, day to day and year to year but the Great Flow is timeless; measured against the scale of infinity. Similarly, while our terms of reference are relative, the Flow is absolute.

I had thought Sambana had been my destination and the conclusion to my quest, but I was wrong. This realization took me on a journey through hell.

Whether it was weeks or months I'm not sure, but in the period that followed burying Sambana and Miss Shinytooth I slipped into a dream world in which I believed they were still alive; and in which past, present and future merged into a continuum at the outer limits of lucidity.

Sambana's simple allegory of a rock suddenly appearing in the path of a boat on the river described the way things were. It was a lunatic situation in which we didn't really know what was going to happen next, and in which the balance of control could shift at any moment.

War is a particular kind of lunacy.

Reality is not logical it merely appears to be so, and the more extreme the situation – as in war – the less logical its appearance.

In extreme situations – as in war – life doesn't follow a peaceful pace and pattern but moves like a torrent, as if the volume of 'normal' experience has been turned up beyond maximum.

The Flow is neither kind nor cruel. These are relative terms. But through its absolute nature the Flow resolves the paradox that underscores mortal life, and that lies at the root of our suffering.

Mama Palma Vini and the boy Jonathan found in the store nursed me while I was in the psychosis of that dream world. When I awoke from it; after Jonathan and I had fought we realized that somehow all we had left was each other.

Jonathan, Pole, Heile, Cape, Scotty and I became newly bonded around a sole intention: to find the perpetrators of the attack on the mission station. Ultimately we did, but that too didn't bring me to the conclusion of my quest.

Neither was I carried to its conclusion in that empty goods wagon on the train across the savannah.

First in Nairobi then in Uganda, I found people with whom I felt a sense of kinship; people with whom I felt comfortable, and with whom I had felt a sense of belonging. I found brotherhood and I found love.

On that train Pole's phantom planted a seed in my heart that carried the promise of healing and the light of hope.

That seed was like the tear on Sambana's face in Giuseppe's infirmary – a kernel holding the promise of new life. It was the flame of a candle, bringing light into the darkness – into my darkness.

In that moment on the train I realized that the spirit of the love I'd known had survived – and, because by then the others were no longer in this world, I was the only person who could carry it.

In the chaos of our fragile circumstances I lost the people

to whom I'd devoted my life but I still carried their love and, like the Flow, it was eternal and the only source of redemption.

The Flow is constant, and so perhaps too our quests are without end in this life.

My story honours the memory of the people I knew – heroes, every one of them.

Each one of our stories, a tiny ripple in the grand scheme of things but, like the orbit of solitary stars set against the infinite scale of the heavens, transcendent in themselves.

EPILOGUE

Many are they who talk to me from the Flow and great are the good things I feel from them; most of all that we should never keep fear as company but make peace our friend and neither should we ever forget that the Flow is good to the lost and the lonely.

To those who are scared it opens its arms; welcoming us to a home we always knew, though one we may have often denied – welcoming us home as our mother and our only destination.

Ultimately there can be no 'just' war because all wars lead to tragic consequences – it's a universal fact; particularly at the level of the individual human life – insignificant in the grand scheme but each with the potential for transcendence.

Each with the potential to experience peace and love

Where is peace to be found... and love?

Always so close by – in our hearts

It was at The Heart that Sambana and Miss Shinytooth died but in my heart they will live forever.

I carry the responsibility for the mistakes I made but also the knowledge that they were born from good and righteous intention. Though regret and a sense of guilt may never leave me completely, through peace and love there is redemption.

For we are human: succeeding, failing, experiencing and
learning – links in a chain framed by The Great Flow.
With my daughters, in the present, on a pine-framed lake
under an azure-blue Swedish summer sky.
I live in peace now and with love in my heart